CONTENTS.

VOL. I.

SECT. I.   Pag.
OF the plan and conduct of the FAERIE QUEENE,   1

SECT. II.
Of Spenser's imitations from old romances, — — 17

SECT. III.
Of Spenser's use and abuse of antient history and mythology, 66

SECT. IV.
Of Spenser's stanza, versification, and language, 113

SECT. V.
Of Spenser's imitations from Chaucer, — — 135

SECT. VI.
Of Spenser's imitations from Ariosto, — — — 198

VOL. II.

SECT. VII.
Of Spenser's inaccuracies, — — — — — — 1

SECT. VIII.
Of Spenser's imitations of himself, — — — — 36

SECT. IX.
Mr. Upton's opinion concerning several passages in Spenser, examined, — — — — — 71

SECT. X.
Of Spenser's allegorical character, — — — — 87

SECT. XI.
Containing miscellaneous remarks, — — — — 114

POSTSCRIPT, — — — — — — 262

ON THE
FAIRY QUEEN
OF
SPENSER.

SECT. I.
Of the plan and conduct of the Fairy Queen.

WHEN the works of Homer and of Aristotle began to be restored and studied in Italy, when the genuine and uncorrupted sources of antient poetry and antient criticism were opened, and every species of literature at last emerged from the depths of Gothic ignorance and barbarity; it might have been expected, that, instead of the romantic manner of poetical composition introduced and established by the Provencial bards, a new and more legitimate taste of writing would have succeeded. With these advantages it was reasonable to conclude, that unnatural events, the machinations of imaginary beings, and adventures entertaining only as they were improbable, would have given place to justness of thought and design, and to that decorum which na-

(2)

ture dictated, and which the example and the precept of antiquity had authorised. But it was a long time before such a change was effected. We find Ariosto, many years after the revival of letters, rejecting truth for magic, and preferring the ridiculous and incoherent excursions of Boyardo, to the propriety and uniformity of the Grecian and Roman models. Nor did the restoration of antient learning produce any effectual or immediate improvement in the state of criticism. Beni, one of the most celebrated critics of the sixteenth century, was still so infatuated with a fondness for the old Provencial vein, that he ventured to write a regular dissertation *, in which he compares Ariosto with Homer.

Trissino, who flourished a few † years after Ariosto, had taste and boldness enough to publish an epic poem‡, written in professed imitation of the Iliad. But this attempt met with little regard or applause for the reason on which its real merit was founded. It was rejected as an insipid and uninteresting performance,

* Comparazione di T. Tasso con Omero e Virgilio, insieme con la difesa dell' Ariosto paragonato ad Omero, &c.

† He died 1550. Ariosto 1535.

‡ L'Italia Liberata di Goti, 1524. It is in blank verse, which the author would have introduced instead of the *Terza* Rima of Dante, or the *Ottava* of Boccace.

having

having few devils or enchantments to recommend it. To Triffino succeeded Taffo, who, in his Gierufaleme Liberata, took the antients for his guides; but was still too fenfible of the popular prejudice in favour of ideal beings, and romantic adventures, to neglect or omit them entirely. He had studied, and acknowledged the beauties of claffical purity. Yet he still kept his first and favourite acquaintance, the old Provencial poets, in his eye. Like his own Rinaldo, who after he had gazed on the diamond fhield of truth, and with feeming refolution was actually departing from Armida and her enchanted gardens, could not help looking back upon them with fome remains of fondnefs. Nor did Taffo's Poem, though compofed in fome meafure on a regular plan, give its author, among the Italians at leaft, any greater fhare of efteem and reputation on that account. Ariofto, with all his extravagancies, was still preferred. The fuperiority of the Orlando Furiofo was at length established by a formal decree of the academicians della Crufca, who, amongst other literary debates, held a folemn court of enquiry concerning the merit of both poems.

Such was the prevailing tafte, when Spenfer projected the Fairy Queen: a poem, which according to the practice of Ariosto, was to confist of allegories, enchantments, and romantic expeditions, conducted by knights, giants, magicians, and fictitious beings. It may be urged, that Spenser made an unfortunate choice, and discovered but little judgment, in adopting Ariosto for his example, rather than Tasso, who had so evidently exceeded his rival, at least in conduct and decorum. But our author naturally followed the poem which was most celebrated and popular. For although the French critics universally gave the preference to Tasso, yet, in Italy, the partisans on the side of Ariosto were by far the most powerful, and consequently in England: for Italy, in the age of queen Elizabeth, gave laws to our island in all matters of taste, as France has done ever since. At the same time it may be supposed, that, of the two, Ariosto was Spenser's favourite; and that he was naturally biassed to prefer that plan which would admit the most extensive range for his unlimited imagination. What was Spenser's particular plan, in consequence of this choice, and how it was conducted, I now proceed to examine.

* The poet supposes, that the FAERIE QUEENE, according to an established annual custom, held a

* See Spenser's Letter to Sir W. Raleigh, &c.

magnificent

magnificent feast, which continued twelve days; on each of which, respectively, twelve several complaints are presented before her. Accordingly, in order to redress the injuries which were the occasion of these several complaints, she dispatches, with proper commissions, twelve different Knights, each of which, in the particular adventure allotted to him, proves an example of some particular virtue, as of holiness, temperance, justice, chastity; and has one complete book assigned to him, of which he is the hero. But besides these twelve knights, severally exemplifying twelve moral virtues, the poet has constituted one principal knight or general hero, viz. PRINCE ARTHUR. This personage represents magnificence; a virtue which is supposed to be the perfection of all the rest. He moreover assists in every book, and the end of his actions is to discover, and win, GLORIANA, or Glory. In a word, in this character the poet professes to pourtray, " THE IMAGE OF A BRAVE KNIGHT PERFECTED IN THE TWELVE PRIVATE MORAL VIRTUES."

It is evident that our author in establishing one hero, who seeking and attaining one grand end, which is GLORIANA, should exemplify one grand character, or a brave Knight perfected in the twelve private
moral

moral virtues, copied the caſt and conſtruction of the antient Epic. But ſenſible as he was of the importance and expediency of the unity of the hero and of his deſign, he does not, in the mean time, ſeem convinced of the neceſſity of that unity of action, by the means of which ſuch a deſign ſhould be properly accompliſhed. At leaſt, he has not followed the method practiſed by Homer and Virgil, in conducting their reſpective heroes to the propoſed end.

It may be aſked with great propriety, how does ARTHUR execute the grand, ſimple, and ultimate deſign, intended by the poet? It may be anſwered, with ſome degree of plauſibility, that by lending his reſpective aſſiſtance to each of the twelve Knights, who patronize the twelve virtues, in his allotted defence of each, ARTHUR approaches ſtill nearer and nearer to Glory, till at laſt he gains a complete poſſeſſion. But ſurely to aſſiſt is not a ſufficient ſervice. This ſecondary merit is inadequate to the reward. The poet ought to have made this " brave Knight" the leading adventurer. ARTHUR ſhould have been the principal agent in vindicating the cauſe of Holineſs, Temperance, and the reſt. If our hero had thus, in his own perſon, exerted himſelf in the protection of the twelve virtues, he might have been deſervedly

deservedly styled the perfect Pattern of all, and consequently would have succeeded in the task assigned, the attainment of Glory. At present he is only a subordinate or accessory character. The difficulties and obstacles which we expect him to surmount, in order to accomplish his final atchievement, are removed by others. It is not he who subdues the dragon, in the first book, or quells the magician Busirane, in the third. These are the victories of St. George and of Britomart. On the whole, the twelve Knights do too much for ARTHUR to do any thing; or at least, so much as may be reasonably required from the promised plan of the poet. While we are attending to the design of the nero of the book, we forget that of the hero of the poem. Dryden remarks, " We " must do Spenser that justice to observe, that mag- " nanimity [magnificence] which is the true character " of Prince Arthur, shines throughout the whole " poem; and succours the rest when they are in di- " stress *." If the magnanimity of Arthur did, in reality, thus shine in every part of the poem with a superior and steady lustre, our author would fairly stand acquitted. At present it bursts forth but seldom, in obscure and interrupted flashes. " To succour the " rest when they are in distress," is, as I have hinted,

* Dedication to the Translation of Juvenal.

a cira circumstance of too little importance in the character of this universal champion. It is a service to be performed in the cause of the hero of the Epic Poem by some dependent or inferior chief, the business of a Gyas or a Cloanthus.

On the whole, we may observe, that Spenser's adventures, separately taken as the subject of each single book, have not always a mutual dependence upon each other, and consequently do not properly contribute to constitute one legitimate poem. Hughes not considering this, has advanced a remark in commendation of Spenser's critical conduct, which is indeed one of the most blameable parts of it. " If we consider the first book as an " entire work of itself, we shall find it to be no irre-" gular contrivance. There is one principal action, " which is completed in the twelfth canto, and the " several incidents are proper, as they tend either to " obstruct or promote it *."

As the heroic poem is required to be one WHOLE, compounded of many various parts, relative and dependent, it is expedient that not one of those parts should be so regularly contrived, and so completely finished, as to become a WHOLE of itself. For the

* Remarks on the Fairy Queen. Hughes's Edit. of Spenser, vol. 1.

mind, being once satisfied in arriving at the consummation of an orderly series of events, acquiesces in that satisfaction. Our attention and curiosity are in the midst diverted from pursuing, with due vigour, the final and general catastrophe. But while each part is left incomplete, if separated from the rest, the mind still eager to gratify its expectations, is irresistibly and imperceptibly drawn from part to part, 'till it receives a full and ultimate satisfaction from the accomplishment of one great event, which all those parts, following and illustrating each other, contributed to produce.

Our author was probably aware, that by constituting twelve several adventures for twelve several heroes, the want of a general connection would often appear. On this account, as I presume, he sometimes resumes and finishes in some distant book, a tale formerly begun and left imperfect. But as numberless interruptions necessarily intervene, this proceeding often occasions infinite perplexity to the reader. And it seems to be for the same reason, that after one of the twelve Knights has atchieved the adventure of his proper book, the poet introduces him, in the next book, acting perhaps in an inferior sphere, and degraded to some less dangerous exploit. But this conduct is highly inartificial: for it destroys that repose which the mind feels

feels after having accompanied a hero, through manifold ſtruggles and various diſtreſſes, to ſucceſs and victory. Beſides, when we perceive him entering upon any leſs illuſtrious attempt, our former admiration is in ſome meaſure diminiſhed. Having ſeen him complete ſome memorable conqueſt, we become intereſted in his honour, and are jealous concerning his future reputation. To attempt, and even to atchieve, ſome petty poſterior enterpriſe, is to derogate from his dignity, and to fully the tranſcendent luſtre of his former victories.

Spenſer perhaps would have embaraſſed himſelf and the reader leſs, had he made every book one entire detached poem of twelve cantos, without any reference to the reſt. Thus he would have written twelve different books, in each of which he might have completed the pattern of a particular virtue in twelve Knights reſpectively: at preſent he has remarkably failed, in endeavouring to repreſent all the virtues exemplified in one. The poet might either have eſtabliſhed TWELVE KNIGHTS without an ARTHUR, or an ARTHUR without TWELVE KNIGHTS. Upon ſuppoſition that Spenſer was reſolved to characteriſe the twelve moral virtues, the former plan perhaps would have been beſt: the latter is defective as it neceſſarily wants ſimplicity. It is an action conſiſting of twelve actions, all equally great and unconnected

(11)

nected between themselves, and not compounded of one uninterrupted and coherent chain of incidents, tending to the accomplishment of one design.

I have before remarked, that Spenser intended to express the character of a hero perfected in the twelve moral virtues, by representing him as assisting in the service of all, till at last he becomes possessed of all. This plan, however injudicious, he certainly was obliged to observe. But in the third book, which is styled the Legend of Chastity, Prince Arthur does not so much as lend his assistance in the vindication of that virtue. He appears indeed; but not as an agent, or even an auxiliary, in the adventure of the book.

Yet it must be confessed, that there is something artificial in the poet's manner of varying from historical precision. This conduct is rationally illustrated by himself †. According to this plan, the reader would have been agreeably surprised in the last book, when he came to discover that the series of adventures, which he had just seen completed, were undertaken at the command of the FAIRY QUEEN; and that the Knights had severally set forward to the execution of them, from her annual birth-day festival. But Spenser, in most of the books, has injudiciously forestalled the first of these particulars; which certainly should have

† Letter to Sir W. Ralegh.

been

been concealed 'till the laft book, not only that a needlefs repetition of the fame thing might be prevented, but that an opportunity might be fecured of ftriking the reader's mind with a circumftance new and unexpected.

But notwithftanding the plan and conduct of Spenfer, in the poem before us, is highly exceptionable, yet we may venture to pronounce, that the fcholar has more merit than his mafter in this refpect; and that the FAIRY QUEEN is not fo confufed and irregular as the Orlando Furiofo. There is indeed no general unity which prevails in the former: but, if we confider every book, or adventure, as a feparate poem, we fhall meet with fo many diftinct, however imperfect, unities, by which an attentive reader is lefs bewildered, than in the maze of indigeftion and incoherence, of which the latter totally confifts, where we feek in vain either for partial or univerfal integrity.

———Cum nec pes nec caput *uni*
Reddatur *Formæ**.————

Ariofto has his admirers, and moft defervedly. Yet every claffical, every reafonable critic muft acknowledge, that the poet's conception in celebrating the MADNESS, or, in other words, defcribing the irra-

* HOR. ART. POET. v. 8.

tional

tional acts, of a hero, implies extravagance and abfurdity. Orlando does not make his appearance till the eighth book, where he is placed in a situation not perfectly heroic. He is discovered to us in bed, defiring to sleep. His ultimate design is to find Angelica. but his pursuit of her is broken off in the thirtieth book; after which there are sixteen books, in none of which Angelica has the least share. Other heroes are likewise engaged in the same pursuit. After reading the first stanza, we are inclined to think, that the subject of the poem is the expedition of the Moors into France, under the emperor Agramante, to fight against Charlemagne; but this business is the most infignificant and inconsiderable part of it. Many of the heroes perform exploits equal, if not superior, to those of Orlando; particularly Ruggiero, who closes the poem with a grand and important atchievement, the conquest and death of Rodomont. But this event is not the completion of a story carried on, principally and perpetually, through the work.

This spirited Italian passes from one incident to another, and from region, to region with such incredible expedition and rapidity, that one would think he was mounted upon his winged steed Ippogrifo. Within the compass of ten stanzas, he is in England and the Hesperides, in the earth and the moon. He begins the
history

history of a knight in Europe, and fuddenly breaks it off to refume the unfinifhed cataftrophe of another in Afia. The reader's imagination is diftracted, and his attention harraffed, amidft the multiplicity of tales, in the relation of which the poet is at the fame inftant equally engaged. To remedy this inconvenience, the compaffionate expofitors have affixed, in fome of the editions, marginal hints, informing the bewildered reader in what book and ftanza the poet intends to recommence an interrupted epifode. This expedient reminds us of the aukward artifice practifed by the firft painters. However, it has proved the means of giving Ariofto's admirers a clear comprehenfion of his ftories, which otherwife they could not have obtained, without much difficulty. This poet is feldom read a fecond time in order; that is, by paffing from the firft canto to the fecond, and from the fecond to the reft in fucceffion: by thus perfuing, without any regard to the proper courfe of the books and ftanzas, the different tales, which though all fomewhere finifhed, yet are at prefent fo mutually complicated, that the incidents of one are perpetually clafhing with thofe of another. The judicious Abbe du Bos obferves happily enough, that " Homer is a geometrician in com-
" parifon of Ariofto." His mifcellaneous contents cannot be better expreffed than by the two firft verfes of his exordium.

Le

Le Donni, i Cavallier, l'Arme, gli Amori,
Le Cortegie, le' audaci Imprese, io canto *.

But it is absurd to think of judging either Ariosto or Spenser by precepts which they did not attend to. We who live in the days of writing by rule, are apt to try every composition by those laws which we have been taught to think the sole criterion of excellence. Critical taste is universally diffused, and we require the same order and design which every modern performance is expected to have, in poems where they never were regarded or intended. Spenser, and the same may be said of Ariosto, did not live in an age of planning. His poetry is the careless exuberance of a warm imagination and a strong sensibility. It was his business to engage the fancy, and to interest the attention by bold and striking images †, in the formation, and the disposition of which, little labour or art was applied. The various and the marvellous were the chief sources of delight. Hence we find our author ransacking alike the regions of reality and romance, of

---

* Orl. Fur. c. 1. s. 1.

† Montesquieu has partly characterised Spenser, in the judgement he has passed upon the English poets, which is not true with regard to all of them. "Leurs poetes auroient plus souvent cette rudesse originale de " l'invention, qu' une certaine delicatesse que donne le gout: on y " trouveroit quelque chose qui approcheroit plu de la force de M. Ange, " que de la grace du Raphael." L'Esprit du Loix. liv. 19. chap. 27. The French critics are too apt to form their general notions of English poetry, from our fondness for Shakespeare.

truth

truth and fiction, to find the proper decorations and furniture for his fairy structure. Born in such an age, Spenser wrote rapidly from his own feelings, which at the same time were naturally noble. Exactness in his poem, would have been like the cornice which a painter introduced in the grotto of Calypso. Spenser's beauties are like the flowers in Paradise.

———Which not nice Art
In beds and curious knots, but Nature boon
Pour'd forth profuse, on hill, and dale, and plain;
Both where the morning sun first warmly smote
The open field, or where the unpierc'd shade
Imbrown'd the noon-tide bowers *.———

If the FAIRY QUEEN be destitute of that arrangement and œconomy which epic severity requires, yet we scarcely regret the loss of these while their place is so amply supplied, by something which more powerfully attracts us: something, which engages the affections the feelings of the heart, rather than the cold approbation of the head. If there be any poem, whose graces please, because they are situated beyond the reach of art, and where the force and faculties of creative imagination delight, because they are unassisted and unrestrained by those of deliberate judgment, it is this. In reading Spenser if the critic is not satisfied, yet the reader is transported.

* Parad. Lost, b. iv. v. 241.

SECT.

SECT. II.

Of Spenser's Imitations from old Romances.

ALthough Spenser formed his FAERIE QUEENE upon the fanciful plan of Ariosto, yet it must be confessed, that the adventures of his knights are a more exact and immediate copy of those which we meet with in old romances, or books of chivalry, than of those which form the Orlando Furioso. Ariosto's knights exhibit surprising examples of their prowess, and atchieve many heroic actions. But our author's knights are more professedly engaged in revenging injuries, and doing justice to the distressed; which was the proper business, and ultimate end of the antient knight-errantry. And thus though many of Spenser's incidents are to be found in Ariosto; such as that of blowing a horn, at the sound of which the gates of a castle fly open, of the vanishing of an enchanted palace or garden after some knight has destroyed the enchanter, and the like; yet these are not more peculiarly the property of Ariosto, than they are common to all ancient romances in general. Spenser's first book is, indeed, a regular and precise imitation of such a series of action as we frequently find in books of chivalry. For instance; A king's daughter applies

applies to a knight, that he would relieve her father and mother, who are closely confined to their castle, upon account of a vast and terrible dragon, that had ravaged their country, and perpetually laid wait to destroy them. The knight sets forward with the lady, encounters a monster in the way, is plotted against by an enchanter, and after surmounting a variety of difficulties and obstacles, arrives at the country which is the scene of the dragon's devastation, kills him, and is presented to the king and queen, whom he has just delivered; marries their daughter, but is soon obliged to leave her, on account of fulfilling a former vow.

It may be moreover observed, that the circumstance of each of Spenser's twelve nights, departing from one place, by a different way, to perform a different adventure, exactly resembles that of the seven knights entering upon their several expeditions, in the well-known romance, entitled the *Seven Champions of Christendom*. In fact, these miraculous books were highly fashionable, and chivalry, which was the subject of them, was still practised and admired, in the age of queen Elizabeth [*].

[*] See Hollinshead's Chronicles, vol. iii. p. 1315.

Among

Among others, there is one romance which Spenser seems more particularly to have made use of. It is entitled, MORTE ARTHUR, *The Lyf of Kyng Arthur, of the noble Knyghtes of the round table, and in thende the dolorous deth of them all.* This was translated into English from the French, by one Sir Thomas Maleory, Knight, and printed by W. Caxton, 1484 *. From this fabulous history our author has borrowed many of his names, viz. Sir Tristram, Placidas, Pelleas, Pellenore, Percivall, and others. As to Sir Tristram, he has copied from this book the circumstances of his birth and education with much exactness. Spenser informs us that Sir Tristram was born in Cornwall, &c.

And Tristram is my name, the only heire
Of good king Meliogras, which did raigne
In Cornewaile. ——— 6. 2. 28.

And afterwards.

——— The countrie wherein I was bred
The which the fertile Lionesse is hight. St. 30.

These particulars are drawn from the romance abovementioned. " There was a knight Meliodas " [Meliogras], and he was lord and king of the " country of Lyones—and he wedded king Markes

* This Book has been reprinted twice or thrice. The last Edition is dated 1634.

D 2 " sister

"fifter of Cornewale." The iffue of which marriage, as we are afterwards told, was Sir Triftram †. Mention is then made in our romance, of Sir Triftram's banifhment from Lyones into a diftant country, by the advice, and under the conduct, of a wife and learned counfellor named Governale. A circumftance alluded to by Spenfer in thefe verfes.

> So taking counfel of a wife man red,
> She was by him adviz'd, to fend me quight
> Out of the countrie, wherein I was bred,
> The which the fertile Lioneffe is hight. 6. 2. 30.

Sir Triftram's education is thus defcribed below. St. 31.

> All which my dayes I have not lewdly fpent,
> Nor fpilt the bloffom of my tender yeares
> In ydleffe, but as was convenient,
> Have trained bene with many noble feres
> In gentle thewes, and fuch like femely leres;
> 'Mongft which my moft delight has always beene
> To hunt the favage chace among my peres
> Of all that raungeth in the foreft greene,
> Of which none is to me unknown that e'er was feene.

> XXXII.
> Ne is there hawke that mantleth her on pearch
> Whether high-tow'ring, or accoafting lowe,

† Book ii. chap. i.

But I the meafure of her flight do fearch,
And all her pray, and all her dyet knowe.

All this is agreeable to what is related in the romance. After mention being made of Triftram's having learned the language of France, courtly behaviour, and fkill in chivalry, we read the following paffage. "As he growed in might and ftrength, he laboured "ever in hunting and hawking; fo that we never read "of no gentleman, more, that fo ufed himfelfe "therein.—And he began good meafures of blowing "of blafts of venery [hunting] and chafe, and of all "manner of vermeins; and all thefe termes have we "yet of hawking and hunting, and therefore the booke "of venery, of hawking and hunting, is called THE "BOOK OF SIR TRISTRAM *." And in another place King Arthur thus addreffes Sir Triftram. "For of "all manner of hunting thou beareft the prife; and of "all meafures of blowing thou art the beginner; and "of all the termes of hunting and hawking ye are "the beginner †.

In Tuberville's treatife of *Falconrie*, &c. Sir Triftram is often introduced as the patron of field-fports. A huntfman thus fpeaks,

Before the King I come report to make,
Then hufhe and peace for noble TRISTRAM's fake ‡.

* Book ii. chap. 3.   † B. ii. c. 91.   ‡ Edit. 4to. 1611. p. 96.

And

And in another place.

> Wherefore who lyſt to learn the perfect trade
> Of venerie, &c.——
> Let him give ear to ſkillfull TRISTRAM's lore [*].

Many of the precepts contained in the BOOK OF SIR TRISTRAM are often referred to in this treatiſe of Tuberville.

From this romance our author alſo took the hint of his BLATANT BEAST; which is there called the QUESTING BEAST §. " Therewithall the King ſaw " coming towards him the ſtrangeſt beaſt that ever " he ſaw, or heard tell off.—And the noyſe was in " the beaſts belly like unto the *Queſtin* of thirtie " couple of houndes." The QUESTING BEAST is afterwards more particularly deſcribed. " That had " in ſhap an head like a ſerpent's head, and a body " like a liberd, buttocks like a lyon, and footed like " a hart; and in his body there was ſuch a noyſe, as " it had been the noyſe of thirtie couple of houndes " *Queſtyn*, and ſuch a noyſe that beaſt made where- " ſoever he went †." Spenſer has made him a much

---

[*] Pag. 40. See alſo Mort. Arth. B. ii. c. 138.
§ B. ii. c. 53.
† He is alſo called the GLATISANT BEAST. ibid. B. ii. c. 98. " Tell them that I am the knight that followeth the *Glatiſant Beaſt*, " that is to ſay, in Engliſh, the QUESTING BEAST, &c."

more

more monstrous animal than he is here reprefented to be, and in general has varied from this defcription. But there is one circumftance in Spenfer's reprefentation, in which there is a minute refemblance, viz.— fpeaking of his mouth,

And therein were a thoufand tongues empight,
Of fundry kindes, and fundry qualities,
Some were of dogs that barked night and day.
And fome, &c. ————————— 6. 12. 27.
So dreadfully his hundred tongues did bray.
5. 12. 41.

By what has been hitherto faid, perhaps the reader may not be perfuaded, that Spenfer, in his BLATANT BEAST, had the QUESTING BEAST of our romance in his eye. But the poet has himfelf taken care to inform us of this: for we learn, from the romance, that certain knights of the round table were deftined to perfue the QUESTING BEAST perpetually without fuccefs: which Spenfer, fpeaking of this BLATANT BEAST, hints at in thefe lines.

Albe that long time after Calidore,
The good Sir Pelleas him took in hand,
And after him Sir Lamoracke of yore,
And all his brethren born in Britaine land,
Yet none of thefe could ever bring him into band.
6. 12. 39.

Sir

(24)

Sir Lamoracke and Sir Pelleas are two very valourous champions of Arthur's round table.

This romance supplied our author with the story of the mantle made of the * beards of knights, and locks of ladies. The last circumstance is added by Spenser.

For may no knight or ladie passe along
That way (and yet they needs must passe that way)
By reason of the streight and rocks among,
But they that ladies lockes do shave away,
And that knights berd for toll, which they for passage pay.
6. 1. 13.

Afterwards,

His name is Crudor, who through high disdaine,
And proud despyght of his selfe-pleasing mynd,
Refused hath to yeald her love againe,
Untill a mantle she for him do find,
With berds of knights, and lockes of ladies lynd.
6. 3. 15.

Thus in MORTE ARTHUR. " Came a messenger— " saying, that king Ryence had discomfited, and

---

* *Immense Beards* seem to have had a wonderful influence in the proper œconomy of an enchantment. Thus we see the barber, who was to personate the Squire of the Princess Micomicona has " una gran barba, &c." D. Quix. parte prim. c. 26. libro 3.
And the Countess of Trifaldi's Squire is described parte 2. lib. vii. c. 36. as wearing " la mas larga, la mas horrida, &c."

" overcomen

" overcomen eleaven knights, and everiche of them
" did him homage; and that was this; they gave
" him their beards cleane flayne of as much as there
" was: wherefore the meffenger came for king Ar-
" thur's berd: for king Ryence had purfeled a man-
" tell with king's beards, and there lacked for one
" place of the mantell. Wherefore he fent for his
" berd; or elfe hee would enter into his lands, and
" brenn and fley, and never leave, till he have thy
" head and beard *." After this paffage we have an
antient ballad †, the fubject of which is this infolent
demand of king Ryence. Drayton §, in his *Polyolbion*,
fpeaks of a coat compofed of the beards of kings. He
is celebrating king Arthur.

As how great Rithout's felf, he flew in his repair
And ravifht Howel's niece, young Helena the fair.
And for a trophie brought the giant's coat away,
Made of the beards of kings.——— ‖

* B. i. c. 24.   † This is alfo printed in P. Enderbury's CAM-
BRIA TRIUMPHANS, Lond. p. 197.
§ I muft take this opportunity of mentioning a circumftance relating to Drayton's tomb in Weftminfter-Abbey, which is erected near
that of Spenfer. Heylin informs us, that Drayton was not buried in
the fouth ile of the church, where his monument is now to be feen;
but under the north wall, near a little door which opens to one of the
prebendal houfes. This Heylin affirms from his own knowledge, he
being invited to Drayton's funeral. *Appeal of Inj. Innocence, pag.* 42.
part 2. fubjoined to Fuller's *Ch. Hift.* Ed. 1655. Bayle would have
expended a folio page in adjufting fuch a point as this.   ‖ Song 4.

VOL I.   E   But

But Drayton, in thefe lines, manifeftly alludes to a paffage in Geoffrey of Monmouth; who informs us, that a Spanifh giant, named Ritho, having forcibly conveyed away from her guard Helena the niece of duke Hoel, poffeffed himfelf of St. Michael's Mount in Cornwall, from whence he made frequent fallies, and committed various outrages; that, at laft, king Arthur conquered this giant, and took from him a certain coat, which he had been compofing of the beards of kings, a vacant place being left for king Arthur's beard *.

And though further proofs of Spenfer's copying this romance are perhaps fuperfluous, I fhall add, that Spenfer has quoted an authority for an antient cuftom from MORTE ARTHUR in his *State of Ireland*. " The " knights in antient times ufed to wear their miftreffes " or lover's fleeve upon their arms, as appeareth by " that which is written of Sir Launcelot, that he wore " the fleeve of the Faire Maid of Afteloth in a tournay: " whereat queen Genever was much difpleafed ‡." This is the paffage. " When queen Genever wift " that *Sir Launcelot* beare the red fleeve of the Faire " Maide of Aftolat, fhe was nigh out of her minde " for anger." †

* Orig. & Geft. Reft. Brit. B. x. 13.
‡ Hughes's Edit. vol. vi. pag. 114. Edit. 1750.   † Mort. Arth. p. 3. ch. 119.

There

There is great reason to conclude, not only from what has already been mentioned concerning Spenser's imitations from this romantic history of king Arthur and his knights, but from some circumstances which I shall now produce, that it was a favorite and reigning romance about the age of queen Elizabeth; or at least one very well known and much read at that time. Spenser in the *Shepherd's Kalendar* has the following passage.

And whither rennes this bevie of ladies bright
    Raunged in a row?
They been all LADIES OF THE LAKE behight,
    That unto her go *.

Upon the words LADIES OF THE LAKE, E. K. the old commentator on the pastorals has left us the following remark. "LADIES OF THE LAKE be nymphes:
" for it was an old opinion among the antient hea-
" thens, that of every spring and fountaine was a
" goddesse the soveraine; which opinion stucke in
" the minds of men not many years since by meanes
" of certain fine fablers, or loose lyers; such as were
" the authors of KING ARTHUR the great.—Who tell
" many an unlawfull leesing of the LADIES OF THE
" LAKE." These fine fablers or loose lyers, are the

* Aprill.

authors

authors of the romance above-mentioned, viz. MORTE ARTHUR, where many miracles are performed, and much enchantment is conducted, by the means and interpofition of the LADY OF THE LAKE. Now it fhould be obferved, that the LADY OF THE LAKE was introduced to make part of queen Elizabeth's entertainment at Kenelworth; as as evidence of which, I fhall produce a paffage from an antient book entitled, A LETTER, *wherein part of the entertainment untoo the queens majefty at Killinworth-caftl in Warwickfheer in this foomers progrefs*, 1575, *is fignified* †. The paffage

† Killingworth-caftle was early made the theatre of romantic gallantries; and was the place where tilts and tournaments, after a long difufe, were re-eftablifhed in their original fplendor by Roger earl of Mortimer, in the reign of Edward I. Thus earl Mortimer, his grandfon, to Q. Ifabell, in Drayton's HEROICAL EPISTLES.

My grandfon was the firft fince Arthur's reign
That the round table rectified again;
To whofe great court at Kenilworth did come
The peerlefs knightood of all Chriftendom. V. 53.

Where fays the note, - - " Roger Mortimer erected the round table at Kenelworth, after the antient order of king Arthur's table, with the retinue of 100 knights, and 100 ladies in his houfe, for the entertaining fuch adventurers as came thither from all parts of Chriftendom." Walfingham mentions the re-eftablifhment of this table at Kenelworth. Hearne has printed from the Red book of the Exchequer, a curious Latin Inftrument of Richard I. concerning the places of holding turnaments in England, where Kenilworth is fpecified among the reft. I will give it in Englifh at length.

Richard

paffage is this. " Her highnefs all along this tilt-yard
" rode unto the inner gate, next the baze coourt of
" of the caftle: whear the LADY OF THE LAKE (fa-
" mous in KING ARTHUR'S BOOK) with too nymphes
" wayting upon her, arrayed all in filkes, attended
" her highnes comming, from the midft of the pool,
" whear upon a moveable ifland bright-blazing with
" torches fhe floting to land, met her majefty with a
" well-penned meter, and matter, after this forte;
" firft of the aunciente of the caftl; who had been
" owners of the fame e'en till this day, moft allways
" in the hands of the earles of Leycefter; how fhe
" had kept this lake fyns king Arthur's dayes, and
" now underftanding of her highnef hither coming,

" Richard by the grace of God, &c. to the Reverend Father in
Chrift, Hubert, Arch. of Cant. &c. greeting. Know, that we have
permitted turnaments to be held in England, in five places; between
Sarum and Wilton, between Warewicke and Kenelingworthe, between
Stamford and Warrinford [Wallingford] between Brakeley and Mixe-
bery, between Blie and Tyke-hill, yet fo that the peace of our land
be not be not broken, nor juftice hindered, nor damage done to our
forefts. And an earl, who fhall turney there, fhall pay us 20 marcs,
and a baron 10 marcs, and a knight, who has land, 4 marcs, and a
knight, who has no land, 2 marcs. No foreigner fhall turney there.
Wherefore we command you, that on the day of the turnament you
fhall provide, at each place, two clerks and [your] two knights, to
receive the oaths from the earls and barons, for their fatisfaction,
concerning the aforefaid fums, &c. " Tho. Hearnii præfat. ad Gul.
Neubrig. Hift. pag. XLIX, L. It is alfo printed in Selden, de Duello.
Richard encouraged thefe exercifes to the higheft degree, æmulous of
the French, who were famous in this way. He was a Troubadour.

" thought

(30)

"thought it both offis and duety; to difcover, in humble wife, her, and her eftate, offring up the fame, hir lake, and power thearin; with promis of repair to the court. It pleafed her highnefs to thank this lady, &c. †"

Gafcoyne ‖ in a little narrative called the "*Princely Pleafures of Kenelworth Caftle,*" gives us fome of the above-mentioned metre, written by Ferrers, one of the contributors to the MIRROR OF MAGISTRATES, of which thefe may ferve as a fpecimen.

I am the lady of this pleafant lake,
Who fince the time of great king Arthur's reigne,
That here with royall court aboade did make,
Have led a lowring life in reftlefs paine;
'Till now that this your third arrival here,
Doth caufe me come abroad, and boldly thus appeare.

For after him fuch ftormes this caftle fhooke,
By fwarming Saxons firft, who fcourgde this land
As forth of this my poole I neer durft looke, &c.

She is afterwards introduced complaining to the queen, that fir Brufe had infulted her for doing an injury to Merlin, an incident related in MORTE

† Written by one Laneham, an attendant on the court.
‖ Works, London, 1576.

ARTHUR;

ARTHUR; and that he would have put her to death had not Neptune delivered her, by concealing her in that lake; from which confinement the queen is afterwards supposed to deliver her, &c.

Without expatiating upon the nature of such a royal entertainment as this, I shall observe from it, that as the LADY OF THE LAKE was a very popular character in the reign of queen Elizabeth, so consequently the romance, which supplied this fiction, was at the same time no less popular. We may add, that it is not improbable that Spenser might allude in the above-cited verses to some of the circumstances in this part of the queen's entertainment; for queen Elisabeth, the Fayre Elisa, is the lady whom the LADIES OF THE LAKE are represented as repairing to, in that eclogue †. Nor is it improbable that this lady was often exhibited upon other occasions: nor is it improper to remark in this place, that Ben. Johnson has introduced her, together with king Arthur and Merlin, in an entertainment before the court of James I. called, PRINCE HENRIES BARRIERS.

† Spenser's pastorals were published about four years after this entertainment. Their first edition is dated 1579. It is a thin quarto; printed in the black letter, with the commentary of E. K. perhaps Edward King.

The above antient letter acquaints us, that the queen was entertained with a fong from this romance, which is a corroborative proof of it's popularity at that time. " A minftrall came forth with a follem fong " warranted for ftory out of KING ARTHUR'S ACTS, " the firft book, 24. whereof I gat a copy, and " that is this.

"So it fell out on a Pentecoft day
"When king Arthur, &c."

This is the fong above hinted at, where mention is made of king Rience demanding the beard of king Arthur. In the fame letter, a gentleman who fhewed fome particular feats of activity before the queen, is faid to be, " very cunning in fens, and hardy as " Gawen." This Gawen was king Arthur's nephew, and his atchievements are highly celebrated in MORTE ARTHUR.

We find Spenfer in another place alluding to the fable of the lady of the lake fo much fpoken of in this romance.

——— A little while
Before that Merlin dyde, he did intend
A brafen wall in compas to compyle
About Cairmardin, and did it commend

Unto

Unto thefe fprights to bring to perfect end;
During which time, the LADIE OF THE LAKE,
Whom long he lov'd, for him in hafte did fend,
Who therefore forſt his workmen to forfake,
Them bound till his returne, their labour not to flake.

3. 3. 9.

In the mean time, thro' that falfe ladies traine
He was furpris'd and buried under beare,
Ne ever to his worke return'd againe.

Thefe verfes are obfcure, unlefs we confider the following relation in MORTE ARTHUR. " The LADY
" OF THE LAKE and Merlin departed; and by the
" way as they went, Merlin fhewed to her many
" wonders, and came into Cornwaile. And alwaies
" Merlin lay about the ladie for to have her favour;
" and fhe was ever paffing wery of him, and faine
" would have been delivered of him; for fhe was
" afraid of him, becaufe he was a divells fon, and
" fhe could not put him away by no meanes. And
" fo upon a time it hapned that Merlin fhewed to her
" in a roche [rock] whereas was a great wonder,
" and wrought by enchauntment, which went under
" a ftone, fo by her fubtile craft and working fhe
" made Merlin to go under that ftone, to let him
" wit of the marvailes there. But fhe wrought fo

VOL. I.　　　　　F　　　　" there

"there for him, that he came never out, for all the
"craft that he could doe *."

Our author has taken notice of a superstitious tradition, which is related at large in this romance.

―――― Good Lucius
That first received christianitie,
The sacred pledge of Chrifts evangelie:
Yet true it is, that long before that day
Hither came Joseph of Arimathie †,
Who brought with him the HOLY GRAYLE, they say,
And preacht the truth; but since it greatly did decay.
2. 10. 53.

The HOLY GRALE, that is, *the real blood* of our blessed Saviour. What Spenser here writes GRAYLE, is often written SANGREAL, or *St. grale*, in MORTE ARTHUR; and it is there said to have been brought into England by Joseph of Arimathea. Many of king Arthur's knights are in the same book represented as adventuring in quest, or in search of the SANGREAL,

---

* B. i. c. 60.
† Concerning the preaching of Joseph of Arimathea there was an old song or legend. "The olde man had an harpe, and there he sung how Joseph of Arimathea came into this land." MORTE ARTHUR B. iii. c. 5. See also c. 38.

or SANGUIS REALIS §. This expedition was one of the firſt ſubjects of the old romance.

This romance ſeems to have extended its reputation beyond the reign of queen Elizabeth. Jonſon, beſides his alluſion to it concerning the LADY OF THE LAKE, mentioned above, hints at it more than once:

> Had I compil'd from Amadis de Gaule,
> Th' Eſplandians, ARTHURS, Palmerins, &c. *

And afterwards, in the ſame poem,

> ——— The whole ſumme
> Of errant knighthood; with the dames and dwarfes,
> The charmed boates, and the enchanted wharfes,
> The TRISTRAMS, LANC'LOTTS, &c.

And Camden † refers to this hiſtory of king Arthur, as to a book familiarly known to the readers of his age. Speaking of the Name TRISTRAM, he obſerves,

§ Hence GRAYLE ſeems to be uſed for the Communion-ſervice in this paſſage of Skelton,

> The Peacock ſo proud,
> Becauſe his voyce is loud;
> He ſhall ſynge the GRAYLE.
>   P. Sparrow, pag. 227. Ed. 1736.

See alſo Davies in *Voce*, and Lwhyd's Dict.
* An execration upon Vulcane, in the Underwood.
† REMAINS, printed 1604. Artic. NAMES.

F 2   "I know

" I know not whether the firſt of his name was " chriſtned by king Arthur's fabler." Again, of Launcelot he ſpeaks, " Some think it to be no " auncient name, but forged by the writer of king " Arthur's hiſtory, for one of his douty knights." And of Gawen, " A name deviſed by the author of " king Arthur's table *."

To this we may add, that Milton manifeſtly hints at it in the following lines,

——— Damſels met in forreſts wide
By knights of Logris, or of Lyones,
Lancelot, Pelleas, or Pellenore §.

Theſe are Sir Lancelot (or Sir Meliot) of Logris; Sir Triſtram of Lyones, and king Pellenore, who are often mentioned in Morte Arthur, and repreſented as meeting beautiful damſels in deſolate forreſts: and probably he might have it in his eye when he wrote the following, as the round table is expreſsly hinted at.

* Rabelais informs us, with the utmoſt gravity, that Launcelot's buſineſs is to roaſt horſes in hell; and that the knights of the round table are employed in ferrying ſouls over Styx; for which they have a fillip on the noſe, and a piece of mouldy bread.
Sect. ii. chapit. 30.
§ Par. Reg. B. ii. v. 359.

Siquando

Siquando indigenas revocabo in carmina reges,
Arturumque etiam sub terris bella moventem,
Aut dicam INVICTÆ *sociali fœdere* MENSÆ
Magnanimos Heroas. ———— ‡

To which we may subjoin,

———— What resounds
In fable, or romance, of Uther's son,
Begirt with British, and Armoric knights †.

Before I leave this romance, I must observe, that Ariosto has been indebted to it; I do not mean, to the old translation, which Spenser made use of. He has drawn his enchanter Merlin from it, and in these verses refers to a particular story concerning him, quoted above. Bradamante is supposed to visit the tomb of Merlin.

Questa è l' antica, e memorabil grotta,
Ch' edificò Merlino il savio mago ;
Che forse recordare odi talhotta,
Dove inganollo la DONNA DEL LAGO.
Il sepolcro è qui giu, dove corrotta
Giace la carne sua ; dove egli vago
Di satisfare a lei, che gliel suase,
Vivo corcossi, e morto ci rimase *.

‡ MANSUS.   † Parad. Lost, i. v. 579.   * C. iii. 10.

Thus

Thus translated by Harrington,

> Heere is the tombe that Merlin erst did make
> By force of secret skill, and hidden art,
> In which sometimes the lady of the lake
> (That with her beauty had bewitcht her hart)
> Did force him enter fondly for her sake;
> And he was by a woman over-reached
> That unto others prophesied, and preached.
>
> xii. 12.
>
> His carkas dead within this stone is bound.

This description of Merlin's tomb, says Harrington in a marginal note, is out of the BOOK OF KING ARTHUR. Ariosto has transferred the tomb from Wales into France. He afterwards feigns, that the prophetical sculpture in Maligigi's cave was performed by Merlin's enchantment.

> *Merlino il savio incantator Britanno*
> *Fe far la fonte, al tempo del re Arturo,*
> *E di cose, ch' al mondo hanno a venire,*
> *La fe da buoni artefici scolpire* ‡.

> —— These whose names appear
> In marble pure, did never live as yet,
> But long time hence, after six hundred yeare,
> To their great praise in princely throne shall sit;

‡ C. 26. 39.

Merlin

(39)

Merlin the Englifh prophet plaſt them here,
In Arthur's time. ——— Harrington.

He alfo mentions fome of the names of the knights of our romance. When Renaldo arrives in Great Britain, the poet takes occafion to celebrate that ifland for its fingular atchievements in chivalry, and for having produced many magnanimous champions; thefe are,

——— Triftano,
Lancillotto, Galaffo, Artu, e Galuano ‖.

Afterwards, in b. 32. Triftram makes a great figure.

From this romance is alfo borrowed Ariofto's tale * of the enchanted cup; which, in Caxton's old tranflation, is as follows. "By the way they met with a "knight, that was fent from Morgan le Faye to king "Arthur; and this knight had a faire horne all gar- "nifhed with gold; and the horne had fuch a virtue, "that there might no ladie or gentlewoman drink of "that horne, but if fhee were true to her hufband; "and if fhee were falfe, fhee fhould fpill all the "drinke; and fhee were true unto her lord, fhee "might drink peaceably, &c." †. Afterwards many tryals are made with this cup. Ariofto's copy begins with the following verfes,

‖ C. 4. S. 22. * B. 2. c. 34. † C. 42. 98.

Ecco

Ecco un Donzello, a chi l' ufficio tocca,
Pon ſu la menſa un bel napo d' or fino.
Di fuor di gemme, e dentro pien di vino.

At laſt a page came in with curtſie low,
And beares a ſtanding cup of gold moſt fine,
Without of gemmes, and full within of wine.

Harrington.

The inimitable Fontaine has new moulded this ſtory from Arioſto, under the title of LA COUPE ENCHANTEE.

As it is manifeſt, from a compariſon of paſſages, that Arioſto was intimately converſant in this romance; ſo I think we may fairly ſuppoſe that he drew from it the idea of his Orlando running mad with jealouſy. In MORTE ARTHUR, Sir Lancelot, ſmitten with a jealous fit, is driven to madneſs, in which ſtate he continues for the ſpace of two years, performing a thouſand ridiculous pranks, no leſs extravagant than thoſe of Orlando; and, like him, at laſt he recovers his ſenſes. A popular and ridiculous romance was a ſufficient hint for what we think a fine effort of poetry.

I had forgot to remark before, that our author has borrowed the name of Materaſta's caſtle from that of Lancelot in MORTE ARTHUR.

—— The

>—— The goodly frame
And stately port of Castle Joyeous. 3, 1, 31.

Lancelot's Castle is styled, by Caxton, Joyous gard, or castle.*

This romance, or at least the stories formed from it, sometimes furnished matter for theatrical exhibitions, as we learn from Shakespeare. " *Shallow.* I remember " at Mile-end Green, when I lay at Clements-inn, " I was Sir Dagonet in Arthur's Show †." Where Theobald remarks, " The only intelligence I have " gleaned of this worthy Wight [*Sir Dagonet*] is from " Beaumont and Fletcher, in their *Knight of the Burn-* " *ing Pestle*." Sir Dagonet is an important character in Morte Arthur. The *magnificent* Arthur bore a considerable part in the old pageants. Thus, relating the marriage of prince Arthur, son of Henry VII. says Bacon, " In the devices and conceits of the triumphs " of this marriage — *you may be sure* that king Arthur " the briton, &c. was not forgotten ‡." In our author's age, we find him introduced among the entertainments exhibited at the splendid reception of lord

---

* So Skelton, in the *Crowne of Lawrell*, p. 53, ed. ut supr. Of the paiants [pageants] that were played in *Joyous Garde*.

† II. P. Hen. IV. Act 3, Sc. 4.

‡ Life of Henry VII, fol. edit. 1730, vol iii, pag. 489.

Leicefter. " Over the entrance of the court-gate was " placed aloft upon a fcaffold, as it had been in a " cloud or fkie, *Arthur of Britaine*, whom they com- " pared to the earl *." Sydney, as appears from a curious converfation between B. Jonfon and Drummond of Hawthornden, recorded by the latter, intended to turn all the ftories of the *Arcadia* into the admired legend of Arthur and his Knights. In his *Defence* of *Poefie* he plainly hints at Caxton's romance. " I dare fay, that *Orlando Furiofo*, or " honeft King ARTHUR [his *hiftory*] will never dif- " pleafe a foldier †."

Caxton's recommendation of this book to the knights of England, conveys a curious picture of the times ‡. " O ye Knyghts of Englond! where is the cuftom " and ufage of noble chyvalry that was ufid in thofe " dayes? What do you now but go to the baynes, " [baths], and playe at dyfe? And fome not well " advifed, ufe not honeft and good rule, agayn all " order of knighthood. Leve this, leve it: And

---

* Holling. Hift. Engl. vol. iii. pag. 1426.

† Ad Calc. The Countefſe of Pembroke's Arcadia, edit. 1638, pag. 558.

‡ From *the boke of the Ordre of Chyvalry, or Knighthood: tranflated out of Frenſhe, and imprinted by William Caxton*. Without date; perhaps 1484. 4to.

" rede

(43)

" rede the noble volumes of *Saynt Greal*, of *Lancelot*,
" of *Galaad*, of *Triſtram*, of *Perſeforeſt*, of *Percyval*,
" of *Gawayne*, and many mo: There ſhall ye ſee
" *manhode, curtoys*, and *gentlenes*. And loke in latter
" dayes of the noble actes ſyth the conqueſt: as in
" king Richard's dayes, *Cuer de Lion*: Edward I. and
" III. and his noble ſones: Syr Robert Knolles, &c.
" Rede Froiſſart. Alſo beholde that victorious and
" noble king, Harry the fifthe, &c." Aſcham however tells us, " I know when God's bible was baniſhed
" the court, and MORTE ARTHUR received into the
" princes chamber *."

In the hall of the caſtle of Tamworth, in Warwick-
ſhire, there is an old rude painting on the wall, of Sir
Lancelot du Lake, and Sir Turquin, drawn in a gi-
gantic ſize, and tilting together. On Arthur's round
table, as it is called, in the caſtle of Wincheſter, ſaid
to be founded by Arthur, are inſcribed in antient characters, the names of twenty-four of his knights, juſt as
we find them in MORTE ARTHUR. This table was
hanging there, in the year 1484, and was even then
very old, being at that time, by tradition, called *Ar-*

---

* Aſcham's *Scholemaſter*, &c. 4to. 1589. b. 1. pag. 25, verſ. There
is a manuſcript Poem by Lydgate, *Of king Arthur and the rounde Table*,
which, I think, was never printed. Bibl. Bodl. Laud. D. 31, f. 64.

thur's round table †. I presume, that in commemoration of Arthur's institution, and in direct imitation of his practice, in later ages, a round table, inscribed with his knights, was usually fixed in some public place, wherever any magnificent turney was held, on which probably the combatants were afterwards feasted. It is well known that tournaments were frequently celebrated in high splendor at Winchester; and this is perhaps one of those very tables. It was partly on account of a round table being thus actually exhibited, that these exercises were familiarly called by the historians of the middle age, *Tabula* or *Mensa Rotunda*. Thus Walter Hemingford, to mention no more instances. " Eodem anno [1280] *Tabula rotunda* tenebatur sump-" tuosè apud Warewyk *."

Some

† Caxton's Preface to Morte Arthur?

* Vit. Edv. I. edit. Hearne, vol. i, pag. 7. See Note, supr. p. 28. It was often a *general* name for a tournament. However, every common tournament was not always strictly called so. " Non ut in hastiludio " illo quod *communiter* et *vulgariter* Torneamentum dicitur, sed po-" tius in illo ludo militari qui mensa rotunda dicitur, vires suas " attemperarent." Matt. Paris, p. 1147. It was perhaps a *peculiar species* of turney, such as was revived at Kenelworth-castle, by earl Mortimer. At such a tournament as this, Chaucer's knight had often been the leading or principal champion:

At Allessandre he was when it was won,
Full oft timis he had *the* borde begon,
In Pruce. - - - - - - - Prol. 51.

But Speght [Gloss. Ch.] says, " that being often among the Knights
" of

Some writers say, that king Arthur first instituted the *round table*, at Cairleon, in Monmouthshire, others at Camelot, in Somersetshire. Both these are mentioned in *Morte Arthur*, as places where Arthur kept his court, with his knights. In the Parish of Lansannan, in Denbighshire, on the side of a stony rock is a circular area, cut out of the rock, having twenty-four seats, which they call Arthur's *round table*. However, it's first and original establishment is generally supposed to have been at Winchester*. Harding, in his *Chronicle* of english kings from Brutus to Edward IV. in whose reign he wrote, tells us, that Uther Pendragon, Arthur's father, founded the *round table* at Winchester, chiefly for the recovery of *Sangreal*, but in commemoration of his marriage with Igerne. Joseph of Arimathea is likewise introduced on this occasion.

    And at the day he weddid her and cround,
And she far forth with child was then begonne,
To comfort her he set the ROUND TABLE
At *Winchester*, of worthiest knights alone,
Approved best in knighthood of their fone,
Which TABLE ROUND, *Joseph of Arimathie*,
For brother made of the SAINT GRAL only.

" of the Teutonic order in Prussia, he was, for his worthiness, placed
" at the upper end of the table, before any, of what nation soever."

* Called *Camelot* in Morte Arthur, 3, 114.

In which he made the fige perilous,
Where none fhould fit, without grete mifchief,
But ONE that fhould be *moft religious*
Of knights all, and of the *round table* CHIEF,
The SAINT GRAL that fhould recover and acheve*.

The ONE *moft religious*, who alone was qualified to fit in the *fige perilous*, and who atchieved and won the SANGREAL, is Sir Galahad, Sir Lancelot's fon †.

In Caxton's romance, king Arthur's dowry with queen Guenever, is faid to be the *round table*, made by her father Uther. Her father, king Leodegrance, fays, " I fhall fend him a gift that fhall pleafe him more, [than lands] for I fhall give him the *table round*, the which *Uther Pendragon gave me* ‡."

There is another antient romance, for fo it may be called, though written in verfe, which Spenfer apparently copies, in prince Arthur's combat with the dragon: it will be neceffary to tranfcribe the whole paffage, which, I believe, will not be thought too long.

* Lond. 1543. edit. Grafton. fol. 61.   † Ibid. 3, 32.
‡ Morte Arthur, i, 45.

It

It fortuned (as faire it then befell)
  Behind his back, vnweeting, where he ſtood
  Of auncient time there was a ſpringing well,
  From which faſt trickled forth a ſiluer flood,
  Full of great vertues, and for med'cine good.
  Whylome, before that curſed dragon got
  That happy land, and all with innocent blood
  Defil'd thoſe ſacred waves, it rightly hot
The well of life : ne yet his vertues had forgot.

                                    I. II. 29.

XXX.

For, unto life the dead it could reſtore,
  And guilt of ſinful crimes cleane waſh away;
  Thoſe that with ſickneſſe were infected ſore,
  It could recure, and ages long decay
  Renew, as it were borne that very day.
  Both Silo this, and Iordan did excell,
  And th'Engliſh Bath, and eke the German Spau,
  Ne can Cephiſe, nor Hebrus match this well :
Into the ſame, the knight (backe overthrowen) fell.

XXXI.

Now gan the golden Phœbus for to ſteepe
  His fierie face in billowes of the weſt,
  And his faint ſteeds watred in Ocean deep,
  Whiles from their iournall labours they did reſt;
  When that infernall monſter having keſt
  His weary foe into that living well,
  Gan high advaunce his broad diſcoloured breaſt
                                    Aboue

Aboue his wonted pitch, with countenance fell,
And clapt his iron wings as victor he did dwell.

XXXII.

Which when his penfiue lady faw from farre,
  Great woe and forrow did her foule affay;
  As weening that, the fad end of the warre,
  And gan to higheft God entirely pray,
  That feared chance from her to turne away;
  With folded hands and knees full lowely bent
  All night fhe watcht, ne once adowne would lay
  Her dainty limbs in her fad dreriment,
But praying ftill did wake, and waking did lament.

XXXIII.

The morrow next gan early to appeare,
  That Titan rofe to run his daily race:
  But early ere the morrow next gan reare
  Out of the fea faire Titans deawy face,
  Vp rofe the gentle virgin from her place,
  And looked all about, if fhe might fpy
  Her loued knight to moue his manly pafe:
  For, fhee had great doubt of his fafety,
Since late fhe faw him fall before his enemy.

XXXIV.

At laft fhe faw, where he vpftarted braue
  Out of the well, wherein he drenched lay;
  As Eagle frefh out of the Ocean waue,
  Where he hath left his plumes all hoary gray,

And deckt himſelf with feathers youthly gay,
Like eyas hauke vp mounts vnto the ſkies,
His newly-budded pineons to aſſay,
And marvailes at himſelf, ſtill as he flies:
So new, this new-borne knight to battell new did riſe.

XXXV.

Whom, when the damned fiend ſo freſh did ſpy,
No wonder if he wondered at the ſight,
And doubted, whether his late enemy
It were, or other freſh ſupplied knight.
He, now to prove his late renewed might,
High brandiſhing his bright deaw-burning blade,
Vpon his creſted ſcalpe ſo ſore did ſmite,
That to the ſkull a yawning wound it made:
The deadly dint his dulled ſenſes all diſmaid.

XXXVI.

I wote not, whether the reuenging ſteele
Were hardened with that holy water dew
Wherein he fell, or ſharper edge did feele,
Or his baptized hands now greater grew;
Or other ſecret vertue did enſew;
Elſe, never could the force of fleſhly arme,
Ne molten metall in his bloud embrew:
For, till that ſtound could never wight him harme,
By ſubtiltie, nor ſleight, nor might, nor mighty charme.

This miraculous manner of healing our author drew from an old poem, entitled, *Sir Bevis of Southampton.*

" What for weary, and what for faint,
" Sir Bevis was neer attaint:
" The dragon followed on Bevis so hard,
" That as he would have fled backward,
" There was a well as I weene,
" And he stumbled right therein.
" Then was Sir Bevis afraid and woe,
" Left the dragon should him sloe:
" Or that he might away passe,
" When that he in the well was.
" Then was the well of such vertu
" Through the might of Christ Jesu,
" For sometime dwelled in that land
" A virgin full of Christes sand,
" That had been bathed in that well,
" That ever after, as men can tell,
" Might no venomous worme come therein,
" By the virtue of that virgin,
" Nor nigh it seven foot and more:
" Then Bevis was glad therefore,
" When he saw the Dragon fell
" Had no power to come to the well.
" Then was he glad without faile,
" And rested awhile for his availe,
" And drank of the water of his fill,
" And then he leapt out of the well,
" And with *Morglay*, his brand

" Assailed

"Affailed the Dragon, I underftand:
"On the Dragon he ftrucke fo faft, &c ‡."

After which the Dragon ftrikes the knight with fuch violence, that he falls into a fwoon, and tumbles as it were lifelefs into the well, by whofe fovereign virtue he is revived.

"When Bevis was at the ground
"The water made him whole and found,
"And quenched all the venim away,
"This well faved Bevis that day."

And afterwards,

"But ever when Bevis was hurt fore,
"He went to the well and wafhed him thore;
"He was as whole as any man,
"And ever as frefh as when he began."

It may be obferved, that this poem of Sir Bevis is in that fhort meafure, which was frequently fung to the harp even in queen Elizabeth's time: a cuftom which probably defcended from the antient bards. The author of the arte of Englifh poefie, printed 1589, thus fpeaks of it. "So on the other fide doth the over-
"bufie and too fpeedy returne of one manner of tune,
"too much annoy, and, as it were, glut the eare,

‡ We have much the fame Miracle in the Seven Champions. 1. 2.

"unlefs

" unless it be in small and popular musickes song by
" these cantabanqui upon benches and barrels heads,
" where they have none other audience than boyes,
" or country fellowes, that passe by them in the streete;
" or else by blind harpers, or such like taverne-min-
" strels, that give a fit of mirth for a groat; and their
" matters being, for the most part, stories of old time;
" as, the *Tale of Sir Topas*, the *Reportes of Bevis of*
" *Southampton*, *Guy of Warwicke*, *Adam Bell*, and
" *Clymme of the Clough*, and such other old *Ro-*
" *mances* or *historical Rhymes*, made purposely for
" recreation of the common people at christmasse
" diners, and brideales; and in tavernes, and alehouses,
" and such places of base resort: also they be used in
" carols and rounds, and such light or lascivious po-
" emes, which are commonly more commodiously
" uttered by these buffoons and VICES in plays, than
" by any other person: such were the rimes of Skelton
" (usurping the name of a poet laureate) being in deede
" but a rude rayling rimer, and all his doings ridicu-
" lous; he used both short distances and short mea-
" sures, pleasing only the popular eare; in our courtly
" MAKER we banish them utterly *." Hence it appears, that Chaucer's pieces, or at least legends drawn
from him, were, at that time, sung to the harp; for

* B. ii. c. 9.

the

the tale, or rime, of Sir Topas is a poem of Chaucer now extant: so the Italians, at present, sing Tasso and Ariosto. Adam Bell and Clym of the Clough were two famous archers: the former of which is, on that account, alluded to by Shakespeare.

The same author, in another place, speaks of this kind of entertainment, by which we may conjecture that it was not always confined to so vulgar an audience. " We ourselves, who compiled this treatise, " have written for pleasure, a little *brief romance*, or " historical ditty, in the English tong, of the isle of " Great-Britaine, in short and long meeters; and by " breaches or divisions to be more commodiously sung " to the harpe in places of assembly, where the com- " pany shall be desirous to hear of old adventures, and " valiaunces of noble knights in times past; as are " those of *king Arthur, and his knights of the round* " *table*; Sir Bevys of Southampton, Guy of War- " wicke, and such other like *."

But to return: the circumstance of the Dragon not being able to approach within seven feet of this well, is imitated by our author St. 49. below, where another water is mentioned, which in like manner preserves the knight.

* B. i. c. 19.

But

But nigh thereto the ever-damned beaft
Durſt not approache, for he was mortal made,
And all that life preſerved did deteſt,
Yet he it oft adventur'd to invade.

We feel a ſort of malicious triumph in detecting the latent and obſcure ſource, from whence an original author has drawn ſome celebrated deſcription: yet this, it muſt be granted, ſoon gives way to the rapture that naturally reſults from contemplating the chymical energy of true genius, which can produce ſo noble a tranſmutation; and whoſe virtues are not leſs efficacious and vivifying in their nature, than thoſe of the miraculous water here diſplayed by Spenſer.

I take this opportunity of mentioning, by the way, that our author, in his Dragon-encounters, circumſtantially adopts all the incidents which occur on this article in romances.

An ingenious correſpondent has communicated to me an old ballad, or metrical romance, called the *Boy and the mantle*, on which Spenſer's conceit of *Florimel's girdle* is evidently founded. A boy brings into king Arthur's hall, at Cairleoln, a magical mantle, by which trial is made of the fidelity of each of the ladies of the
ſeveral

several knights [*]. But this fiction is as manifestly taken from an old french piece, entitled, *Le Court Mantel*; part of which is quoted by M. de la Curne de Sainte Palaye [†], in his learned and entertaining memoirs of ancient chivalry, and who informs us, that it is formed on the tale of the *Enchanted Cup*. Most of these old romantic stories in english, I presume, first existed in french or italian.

Several other incidental imitations of romance, will be pointed out occasionally. As to Spenser's original and genealogy of the fairy nation, I am inclined to conjecture, that part of it was supplied by his own inexhaustible imagination, and part from some fabulous history.

He tells us, (b. 2. 10. 70.) that man, as first made by Prometheus, was called ELFE, who wandering over the world, at length arrived at the gardens of Adonis, where he found a female, whom he called FAY. *Elfe*, according to Junius, is derived from the runic *Alfur*; who likewise endeavours to prove, that the saxons called the ELFES, or spirits, of the Downs, *Dunelfen*; of the Fields, *Feldelfen*; of the Hills,

[*] Manuscript Collection of old Ballads, No. 89.
[†] A Paris, 1760, 12mo, tom. prem. pag. 119.

Muntelfen;

Muntelfen; of the Woods, *Wudelfen,* &c*. ELFE, signifies *quick.* FAY, or FAIRY, I shall explain hereafter.

The issue of ELFE and FAY were called *Fairies,* who soon grew to be a mighty people, and conquered all nations. Their eldest son Elfin governed America, and the next to him, named Elfinan, founded the city of Cleopolis, which was enclosed with a golden wall by Elfiline. His son Elfine overcame the Gobbelines; but, of all Fairies, Elfant was most renowned, who built Panthea, of crystal. To these succeeded Elfar, who slew two brethren-giants; and to him Elfinor, who built a bridge of glass over the sea, the sound of which was like thunder. At length Elficleos ruled the Fairy land with much wisdom, and highly advanced it's power and honour: He left two sons, the eldest of which, fair Elferon, died a premature death, his place being supplied by the mighty Oberon; a prince, whose " wide memorial" still remains; and who dying, left Tanaquil to succeed him by will, she being also called *Glorian,* or GLORIANA.

In the story of Enfinel, who overcame the Gobbelines, he either alludes to the fiction of the Guelfes

---

* See Junius, Etymolog. in ELFE. Etymologists greatly differ about the word.

and

Gibbelines in Italy; or to another race of fairies, called *Goblins*, and commonly joined with *Elfes*. His friend and commentator, E. K. remarks*, that our *Elfes* and *Goblins* were derived from the two parties Guelfes and Gibbelines. This etymology I by no means approve. The mention of it however may serve to illustrate Spenser's meaning in this passage. Elfinan perhaps is king Lud, who founded London, or Cleopolis.

> In which the fairest FAERIE queene doth dwell.
>
> 1. 10. 58.

Elfant built her palace *Panthea*, probably Windsor-castle. The bridge of glass may mean London-bridge. But these images of the golden wall, the crystal tower, &c. seem to be all adopted from romance. At least, they all flow from a mind strongly tinctured with romantic ideas. In the latter part of this genealogy, he has manifestly adumbrated some of our english princes. Elficleos is king Henry VII. whose eldest son, prince Arthur, died, at sixteen years of age, in Ludlow-castle; and whose youngest son Oberon, that is Henry VIII. succeeded to the crown, marrying his brother Arthur's widow, the princess Katharine. This Spenser particularly specifies in these verses:

---

* Eclogue JUNE.

Whofe emptie place, the mightie Oberon
Doubly fupplide, in SPOUSALL and DOMINION.

2. 10. 75.

And that the fame of this king was very recent in our author's age, is obvious.

It is remarkable that Spenfer fays nothing of Edward VI. and queen Mary, who reigned between Henry VIII. and queen Elizabeth; but that he paffes immediately from Oberon to Tanaquil, or GLORIANA, i. e. Elizabeth, who was excluded from her fucceffion by thofe two intermediate reigns. There is much addrefs and art in the poet's manner of making this omiffion.

He dying left the faireft Tanaquill,
Him to fucceed therein by his laft will;
Fairer and nobler liveth none this howre,
Ne like in grace, ne like in learned fkill.

ibid.

As to the Fairy QUEEN, confidered apart from the race of fairies, the notion of fuch an imaginary perfonage was very common. Chaucer, in his *Rime of Sir Thopas*, mentions her, together with a fairy land: and Shakefpeare, the poet of popular fuperftition, has introduced her in the *Midfummer-night's Dream*. She was

was supposed to have held her court in the highest magnificence, in the reign of king Arthur; a circumstance, by which the transcendent happiness of that golden age, was originally represented in it's legendary chronicles. Thus Chaucer:

> In the old dayis of the king Arthure,
> Of which the britons speken great honour;
> All was this lond fulfillid of fayry:
> The ELF-QUENE, with her jolly company,
> Daunsid full oft in many a grene mede:
> This was the old opinion, as I rede*.

Hence too we find, that Spenser followed the established tradition, in supposing his *Fairy Queen* † to exist in the age of Arthur.

In

---

* Wife of Bath's Tale, ver. 857. Urry's edit. fol.

† It appears from John Marston's satires, entitled the SCOURGE of VILLANIE, *three bookes of satyres*, and printed in the year 1598, that our Author's FAERIE QUEENE occasioned many publications in which fairies were the principal actors, viz.

> Go buy some ballad of the FAERY KING.
> *In Lectores.*

And in another place.

> ---- At length some wonted sleepe doth crowne
> His new-falne lids; dreames, straight tenne pound to one
> Out-steps some FAERY with quick motion,
> And tells him wonders of some flowrie vale - - - -
> Awakes, straite rubs his eyes, and prints his tale. B. 3. sat. 6.

In Chaucer's *Rime of Sir Thopas*, mentioned above, the knight, like Spenser's Arthur, goes in search of a *Fairy Queen*.

And I have seen a romance, which seems to have been written soon after Spenser's poem, entitled, The RED-ROSE KNIGHT; where the knight, after the example of prince Arthur, goes in search of the FAIRY QUEEN.

The satires above-mentioned contain many well-drawn characters, and several good strokes of satirical genius, but are not upon the whole so finished and classical as bishop Hall's, the first part of which were published about a year before these. Among other passages the following struck me, as being a good deal in the strain of the beginning of Milton's *L'Allegro*.

> Sleepe, grim reproof; my jocund muse doth sing
> In other keyes to nimble fingering;
> Dull sprighted melancholy leave my braine,
> To hell, Cimmerian night! in lively vaine
> I strive to paint; then hence all darke intent,
> And sullen frowns; come sporting merriment,
> Cheeke-dimpling laughter, &c.   B. 3. sat. 10.

From these satires we may learn also how popular a play Romeo and Juliet was in those days. He is speaking to a wit of the town.

> Luscus, what's playd to day? - - - faith now I know
> I sett thy lips abroach, from whence doth flow
> Nought but pure JULIET AND ROMEO.   Ibid.

Langbaine (Dram. Poets pag. 351.) informs us, that these satires, now forgotten, rendered Marston more eminent than his dramatic poetry. Two years after these, viz. 1600, another collection of satires appeared, written by W. Rowlands, which are by no means contemptible. These are entitled, *The Letting of Humours Blood in the Head-vaine*. So that bishop Hall was not without some followers in the species of poetry which he had newly revived.

An

> An ELF-QUENE well I love, I wis,
> For in this world no woman is,
>   Worthy to be my make;
> All othir womin I forfake,
> And to an ELF-QUENE I me take
>   By dale and eke by doune.
> Into his faddle he clombe anone,
> And pricked over ftyle and ftone
>   An ELF-QUENE to efpie,
> Till he fo long had ridden and gone,
> That he fonde in a privie wone,
>   The countre of FAIRIE.

He then meets a terrible giant, who threatens him with deftruction, for entering that country, and tells him;

> Here wonnith the QUENE of FAIRIE,
> With harpe, and pipe, and fimphonie,
>   Within this place and boure;
> The Child faid, alfo mote I the
> To morrow woll I metin The
>   Whan I have mine armoure *.

In Chaucer it appears that *Fairy-land*, and *Fairies*, were fometimes ufed for hell, and it's ideal inhabitants. Thus in the *Marchant*'s *Tale*.

* V. 3299, et feq. Urry's edit, ut fupr.

Pluto

(62)

Again.
Pluto that is king of FAYRIE.

Proserpine and all her FAYRIE.

In the same.

And I, quoth the Quene, [Proserpine] am of FAYRIE.

In the *Knight's Tale*, when the brazen horse was brought into Cambuscan's hall,

It was of FAYRIE, as the people deem'd *.

That is, " the people thought this wonderful horse " was the work of the devil, and made in hell." And in the romance of the *Seven Champions*, Proserpine is called the FAIRY *Queen*, and said " to sit crowned a- " mongst her FAYRIES †." In *Harsenet's Declaration* ‡, Mercury is called " Prince of the FAIRIES."

This fiction of the *Fairies*, is supposed to have been brought, with other fantastic extravagancies of the like nature, from the eastern nations, while the european christians were engaged in the holy war; those

* V. 221.
† Part 1. ch. 16.
‡ *Of Popish Imposture*, &c. 1602. pag. 57. ch. 12.

expeditions

expeditions being the firſt ſubjects of the elder romance. Theſe are the words of one who has ſhewn his maſterly ſkill and penetration in every part of literature. "Nor "were the monſtrous embelliſhments of enchantments, "&c. the invention of the romancers; but formed upon "*eaſtern tales,* brought thence by *travellers* from their "*cruſades and pilgrimages,* which indeed have *a caſt* "*peculiar to the wild imagination of the eaſtern people* *". That the fairies, in particular, came from the eaſt, the teſtimony of M. Herbelot will more fully confirm; who tells us, that the perſians call the Fairies *Peri,* and the arabs *Ginn*; that they feign, there is a certain country inhabited by them, called *Ginniſtian,* which anſwers to our *Fairy-land*; and that the antient romances of Perſia, are full of *Peri* or *Fairies* †. See alſo *Ginn,* or *Gian,* in Herbelot; under the latter of which, that learned orientaliſt further informs us, that there is an arabian book, entitled, "Pieces de corail

* Supplement to the Tranſl. Pref. ad Jarvis's Don Quixotte.

† Littleneſs is not always implied in *Fairy.* Thus we have *Morgan* le FAY, *Morgan* the FAIRY, one of the queens in *Morte Arthur,* an ELFIN *Lady.* She is called *Morgan la* FEE in the french romance, "*La* TABLE RONDE, *autrement dit* LAUNCELOT *du* LAKE," in two folio volumes: The Firſt of which was printed at Rouen, 1428, by John le Bourgeois. The Second, at Paris, in the ſame year, by John de Pre. They are ſaid [fol. ult. vol. 2.] to be extracted from many true hiſtories, by GUALTIER DE MAP. There is a french romance of the Atchievement of the SANGRAAL, by ROBERT DE BORRON.

"amaſſées

"amassées sur ce qui regarde le GINNES, ou "Genies."

The notions however, so essential to books of chivalry, of giants, necromancers, enchantments, &c. were perhaps established, although not universally, in Europe, before the time of the crusades. All the *Sagas*, or antient islandic histories, are full of them. The Fairies, in particular, held a very important rank in the old Celtic mythology*. The northern nations called them *Duergar*, or *Dwarfs*. Thus the sword *Tirfing*, in the scaldic dialogue between Hervor and Angantyr, is called *Duerga Smidi*, the work of the *Dwarfs* †. This strengthens the hypothesis of the northern part of Europe, particularly Scandinavia, being peopled by colonies from the east, under the command of their general, or god, ODIN. It is well known, how strongly the superstitious belief of spirits, or invisible agents, assigned to different parts of nature, prevails even in Scotland at this day.

Our old romantic history supposes, that Arthur still reigns in Fairy-Land, from which he will one day re-

* See Hervarer Saga of Olaus Verelius, fol. pag. 44, 45. And Hickes's Thesaur. tom. 2. pag. 311, et seq. [per H. Wanley.] See also what is said above, concerning ELFE.

† Hickes's Thesaur. vol. 1. pag. 193. cap. 23.

turn

turn to Britain, and reeſtabliſh the round table in it's original ſplendor.

> He is a king ycrownid in *Fairie*,
> With ſcepter, and ſword: and with his regally
> Shall reſort as lord and ſoveraigne
> Out of *Fairie*, and reigne in Britaine;
> And repair again the old round table.
> By propheſy Merlin ſet the date [*].

The ſame tradition is mentioned by Cervantes in Don Quixote [†].

Many other examples might be alledged, from which it would be more abundantly manifeſted, that our author's imagination was entirely poſſeſſed with that ſpecies of reading, which was the faſhion and the delight of his age. The lovers of Spenſer, I hope, will not think I have been too tedious in a diſquiſition, which has contributed not only to illuſtrate many particular paſſages in their favorite poet, but to diſplay the general caſt and colour of his poem. Some there are, who will cenſure what I have collected on this ſubject, as both trifling and unintereſting; but ſuch readers can have no taſte for Spenſer.

[*] Lydgate, Fall of Princes. b. 8. ch. 25.   [†] Part I. ch. 5.

SECT. III.

Of Spenser's Use and Abuse of antient History and Mythology.

AS Spenser sought to produce surprise by extravagant incidents and fantastic descriptions, great part of classical history and mythology afforded ample materials for such a design, and properly coincided with the general aim of his romantic plan. He has accordingly adopted some of their most extraordinary fictions, in many of which he has departed from the received tradition, as his purpose and subject occasionally required or permitted. But with regard to our author's misrepresentation of antient fable, it may be justly urged, that from those arguments which are produced against his fidelity, new proofs arise in favour of his fancy. Spenser's native force of invention would not suffer him to pursue the letter of prescribed fiction, with scrupulous observation and servile regularity. In many particulars he varies from antiquity, only to substitute new beauties; and from a slight mention of one or two leading circumstances in antient fable, takes an opportunity to display some new fiction of his own coinage. He sometimes, in the fervour of composition, misrepresents these matters through

through haste and inattention. His allusions to antient history are likewise very frequent, which he has not scrupled to violate, with equal freedom, and for the same reasons.

B. i. c. i. s. xxxvii.

A bold bad man, that dar'd to call by name
Great Gorgon. — — —

Dr. Jortin * has multiplied instances by which it appears, that the antients were superstitiously fearful of uttering the name of Gorgon or Dæmogorgon. I shall add, that they were no less afraid of calling the *Furies* by their names.

Electra, in Euripides, says of the Furies, that tormented her brother:

— — ONOMAZEIN γαρ αιδυμαι θεας
Ευμενιδας, 'αι τονδ' εξαμιλλωνlαι φοβω †.

—— *Verear enim nominare*
Deas Eumenidas, quæ eum certatim perterrent.

And in another scene, Orestes says,

Εδοξ' ειδειν τρεις νυκlι προςφερεις κορας.

Visus sum mihi videre tres puellas noëti similes.

* See Remarks on Spenser's Poems. † Orestes, v. 37.

Whom Menelaus anfwers:

Οιδ' ας ελεξας, ΟΝΟΜΑΣΑΙ δ' ȣ ϦȣλοΜαι *.

Novi quas dixifti; nominare autem nolo.

Below, we have the fame fuperftition concerning Hecate:

> And threatned unto him the dreaded name
> Of Hecate. — — — ft. 3.

But it would perhaps be difficult to produce any antient evidence, either that Hecate's name was feared in general, or that Morpheus particularly, was afraid of uttering or hearing it. Our author, with great force of fancy, feigns fuch another circumftance as this, concerning Merlin.

> The fiends do quake, when any him to them does name.
> 3. 3. 11.

Though perhaps this is not more expreffive of Merlin's diabolical power, than what fome of the runic hiftorians mention of a fwedifh enchanter, viz. That he could blunt the edge of the weapons of his enemies only by looking at them, and that he could make hell a light place.

* Ibid. 430.

He

B. i. c. iv. f. xxx.

He is defcribing *Envy.*

— — — Still did chaw,
Between his cankred teeth a venomous toad,
That all the poifon ran about his jaw.

Ovid feigns*, that *Envy* was found eating the flefh of vipers, a fiction not much unlike Spenfer's picture. But our author has heightened this circumftance to a moft difgufting degree: for he adds, that the poifon ran about his jaw. This is perhaps one of the moft loathfome images which Spenfer has given us; though he paints very ftrongly, 1. 1. 20.

——— She fpewd out of her filthy maw,
A flood of poifon horrible and black;
Full of great lumps of flefh and gobbets raw,
Which ftunk fo vilely, that it forc'd him flack
His grafping hold. ——— ———

As alfo in the difcovery of Duessa, 1. 8. 47. 48. He is likewife very indelicate, where he fpeaks of Serena's wounds.

For now her wounds corruption 'gan to breed.

And to forbear difagreeable citations, fee 7. 7. 31. and 7. 7. 40. The truth is, the ftrength of our au-

* Met. ii. v. 76.

thor's imagination could not be suppressed on any subject; and, in some measure, it is owing to the fulness of his stanza, and the reiteration of his rhymes, that he describes these offensive objects so minutely.

But to return to his *Envy*. This personage is again introduced, 5. 12. 29. chewing a snake, of which a most beautiful use is made, st. 39.

> Then from her mouth the gobbet she does take,
> The which whyleare she was so greedily
> Devouring; even that half-gnawen snake;
> And at him throwes it most despitefully:
> The curfed serpent, though she hungrily
> Earst chawd thereon, yet was not all so dead,
> But that some life remained secretly,
> And as he past before withouten dread,
> Bit him behind, that long the mark was to be read.

It may be objected, that Spenser drew the thought of *Envy* throwing her Snake at Arthegall, from Alecto's attack upon Amata.

*Huic Dea cæruleis unum de crinibus anguem
Conjicit, inque sinus præcordia ad intima condit *.*

But Spenser's application of this thought is surely a stronger effort of invention than the thought itself.

* Æn. vii. v. 346.

The

The rancour, both of *Envy* and of her Snake, could not have been expressed by more significant strokes. Although the snake was her constant food, yet she was tempted to part with her only sustenance, while she could render it an instrument of injuring another; and although the snake, by being thus constantly fed upon, was nearly dead, *some life*, as he finely says, *remaining secretly*, yet it's natural malignity enabled it to bite with violence.

B. i. c. v. s. xxxix.

—— His rash fire began to rend
His haire, and hastie tongue that did offend.

Theseus did not rend his tongue on this occasion. Dr. Jortin is willing to excuse our author for this mistake, by supposing an elleipsis, viz. *He began to rend his hair*, and [to blame or curse] *his tongue*. Spenser is indeed full of elleipses, yet he has seldom been guilty of one so hard as this. I should therefore think, that this passage ought not to be referred to our author's elleipses, but to that fault which he so often commits, the misrepresentation of antient story. Besides, the words *that did offend*, joined with *hastie tongue*, seem to be given by the poet as an express reason why he rent it.

B. i.

(72)

B. i. c. vi. f. xiv.

Sylvanus is here introduced:

────── ────── His weake fteps governing,
And aged limbes on cypreffe ftadle ftout.

I do not remember that Sylvanus is any where defcribed as *infirm* with old age. Neither would the young cyprefs tree which he carried in his hand, a fapling, or fmall plant torn up by the root, have ferved for this ufe. Virgil addreffes him;

── *Teneram ab radice ferens, Sylvane, cupreſſum**.

B. i. c. vii. f. xvii.

── ── ── The renowned fnake
Which great Alcides in Stremona flew,
Long-foftred in the filth of Lerna lake.

Hercules flew the hydra in the lake of Lerna, between Mycenæ and Argos. *Stremona* is no where to be found, which he probably put for *Strymon*, a river of Macedonia, in the confines of Thrace. But to read *Strymon* here, would no more agree with the hiftory than the metre.

B. ii. c. iv. f. xli.

── ── Sonne of Erebus and Night.

* Georg. i. v. 20.

Spenfer

Spenser is just to mythology in representing Erebus and *Night* as married. In another place, this address is made to Night.

— — Black Erebus thy husband is.   3. 4. 55.

In these lines of Milton,

> Hence loathed *Melancholy*,
> Of CERBERUS and blackest *Midnight* born,

Mr. Upton substitutes Erebus instead of *Cerberus*. The alteration is ingenious; and to his defence of it he might have added, that Milton, in more than one of his juvenile poems, has given us the true genealogy.

> *Nox senis amplexus* EREBI *taciturna petivit* *.

Again.

> *Non est, ut arbitraris elusus miser,*
> *Mors atra* NOCTIS *filia,*
> EREBOVE *patre creta* †.

And in his Prolusions. "*Cæterum nec desunt qui Æthera et Diem itidem* EREBO NOCTEM *peperisse tradunt* ‡." But after all, without insisting on the material circumstance of two editions of this poem being printed

---

* In Quintum Novemb.
† In Obitum Præsul. Eliens.
‡ *An Nox utrum Dies*, &c. Birch's Edit. vol. 2. pag. 585.

in the life-time, and under the infpection, of Milton, in both of which *Cerberus* is found, I an inclined to think, that he certainly wrote *Cerberus*. Full of the idea of the loathfomenefs of *Melancholy*, he feems to have chofen two the moft deteftable parents for fo foul a demon, that his imagination could fuggeft. And it is to be further obferved, that he does not fay *Midnight* fimply, but *blackeſt* midnight, an epithet by which he feelingly fignifies his abhorrence of the offspring of this infernal pair, and the propriety and confiftency of her being leagued with the monfter CERBERUS.

But to return to Spenfer. — He is alfo exact in his mythology concerning *Night*, in the following verfes.

O thou moſt antient grandmother of old,
More old than Jove, whom thou at firſt didſt breed.

1. 5. 22.

Thus Orpheus, in his Hymn to *Night*.

ΝΥΚΤΑ θεων γενετειραν αεισομαι, ηδε κ) ανδρων,
ΝΥΞ γενεσις παντων. — — —

Noctem *deorum genetricem cantabo atque hominum*,
Nox *genetrix omnium*. — — —

He afterwards fays of her:

Which waſt begott in Dæmogorgon's hall.

That

That is, in *Chaos,* who is the parent of *Night,* according to Hesiod.

Εκ ΧΑΕΟΣ δ' ΕΡΕΒΟΣΤΕ μελαιναῖε Νυξ εγενονῖο *.

A Chao autem Erebus *atraque* Nox *gignebantur.*

Spenser makes *Night* the mother of *Falshood,* according to Hesiod.

—— —— Though I the mother be
Of *Falseshood.* —— —— f. 27. *inf.*

Νυξ ὀλοη μεῖα την δ' ΑΠΑΤΗΝ τεκε †.

Nox perniciosa post illam Fraudem *peperit.*

Spenser gives *Night* a chariot and horses, for which he has the authority of many antient poets. Without citing the particular passages, which are frequent and obvious, I shall take occasion to remark, that what Spenser says of the *horses* of *Night,* in all probability, tempted Milton's fancy to go further, and to give them names.

Thus Spenser.

And cole-black steeds yborne of hellish broode,
That on their rustie bits did champ as they were wood.
1. 5. 20.

* Theog. 123.   † Ibid. 224.

And afterwards.

> Her twyfold teme, of which two black as pitch,
> And two were brown, yet each to each unlitch.
> 1. 5. 28.

Milton's lines are these.

> Nox *senis amplexus* Erebi *taciturna reliquit,*
> *Præcipitesque impellit* Equos, *stimulante flagello:*
> *Captum oculis* Typhlonta, Melanchætemque *ferocem,*
> *Atque Acherontæo prognatam patre* Siopem
> *Torpidam, et hirsutis horrentem* Phrica *capillis* *.

It is at the same time not less probable, that in describing these, he thought of the horses of the Sun, which are named in Ovid; as are the horses of Pluto in Claudian †. Milton, in the same poem, had an eye to another passage in Spenser; who having descibed the personages that sate by the highway leading to hell, adds this fine image.

> And over them sad *Horror* with grim hewe,
> Did alwaies sore, beating his iron wings.   2. 7. 2.

Milton, after mentioning some of the same allegorical beings, adds,

> — *Exanguisque locum circumvolat* HORROR ‡.

* In Quint. Novemb. v. 151.   † Rapt. Proserp. 1. 285.
‡ Ibid. v. 148.

Among

Among thefe beings Milton's defcription of Phonos, or Murder, whom he couples with Prodotes, or Treafon, is remarkably beautiful.

Ipfi etiam pavidi latitant penetralibus antri
Et Phonos et Prodotes ; nulloque fequente per antrum,
Antrum horrent, fcopulofum, atrum feralibus umbris,
Diffugiunt fontes, et retro lumina vertunt.

But, I think it is equalled by Fletcher's figure of *Phonos*, in his forgotten poem, called the *Purple Ifland*.

> Laft of this rout the favage Phonos went,
> Whom his dire mother nurft with human blood;
> And when more age and ftrength more fiercenefs lent,
> She taught him in a darke and defart wood,
> With force and guile poore paffengers to flay,
> And on their flefh his barking ftomach ftay,
> And with their wretched blood his fiery thirft allay.
>
> Ten thoufand Furies on his fteps awaited,
> Some fear'd his harden'd foul with Stygian brand,
> Some with black terrors his faint confcience baited,
> That wide he ftar'd, and ftarched hair did ftand;
> The firft-borne Man ftill in his mind he bore,
> Foully array'd in guiltleffe brother's gore,
> Which for revenge to heaven from earth did loudly roar[*].

[*] Cant. 7. ft. 69. 71.

It is observable, that this little poem of Milton, as containing a council, conspiracy, and expedition, of Satan, may be looked upon as an early prelusion of his genius, to the subject of the *Paradise Lost*.

B. ii. c. vii. f. liii.

The garden of Proserpina this hight,
And in the midst thereof a silver seat,
With a thick arbor goodly overdight,
In which she often us'd from open heat
Herselfe to shroud, and pleasures to entreat.
Next thereunto did growe a goodly tree,
With branches broad disspred and body great,
Cloathed with leaves that none the wood mote see,
And loden all with fruit, as thick as it might be.

liv.

Their fruit was golden apples glistring bright.

This mythology is drawn from Claudian. Pluto consoles Proserpine with these promises.

— — — — *Nec mollia desunt*
Prata tibi: zephyris illic melioribus halant
Perpetui flores, quos nec tua protulit **Enna.**
Est etiam lucis arbor *prædives opacis,*
Fulgenti virides ramos curvata metallo.

Hæc

Hæc tibi sacra datur; fortunatumque tenebis
Autumnum, et fulvis *semper ditabere* pomis*.

The golden fruit, and a *silver stoole*, are afterwards offered to the knight by Mammon, as objects of temptation.

<blockquote>
―― Thou fearfull foole,
Why takest not of that same fruit of gold,
Ne sittest downe on that same silver stoole,
To rest thy weary person in the shadow coole?
</blockquote>

Ovid relates, that Proserpine would have been restored to her mother Ceres, had she not been observed by Ascalaphus to pluck a radiant apple from a tree which grew in her garden; the same, I suppose, which Claudian speaks of in the verses just quoted.

―― ―― Cereri certum est educere natam:
Non ita fata sinunt; quoniam jejunia virgo
Solverat, et cultis dum simplex errat in hortis
Puniceum *curvâ decerpserat arbore* pomum †.

From these verses, Spenser seems to have borrowed, and to have adapted to his present purpose, the notion that these golden apples were prohibited fruit. The *silver stoole* is added from his own fancy, and is a *New Circumstance of* TEMPTATION. His own allegorising

* Rapt. Pros. l. 2. v. 290.   † Met. l. 5. v. 533.

invention

invention has also feigned, that the plants which grew in the garden of Proserpine, were,

— Direful deadly blacke, both leaf and bloom,
Fit to adorn the dead, and deck the dreary toomb.
ft. 51.

Whereas Claudian describes this garden as filled with flowers more beautiful than those of Enna. Nor is he less attentive to the antient fabulists, where he tells us, that the tree of the Hesperides sprung from this of Proserpine; that these were thrown in the way of Hippomanes and Atalanta, ft. 54; and that those with which Acontius won Cydippe, and which Ate flung among the gods, were gathered from Proserpine's tree, ft. 55. He adds, that the branches of this tree overspread the river Cocytus, in which Tantalus was plunged to the chin, and who was perpetually catching at it's fruit. Homer relates, that many trees of delicious fruit waved over the lake in which Tantalus was placed; but it does not appear from Homer, that Tantalus was fixed in Cocytus, but in some lake peculiarly appropriated to his punishment.

Εςαοῖ' εν ΛΙΜΝΗ.

Spenser has also made another use of Cocytus; That the shores of this river eternally resounded with the shriek shrieks of damned ghosts, who were doomed to suffer an everlasting immersion in it's loathsome waters. Cocytus, says antient fable indeed, must be passed, before there is any possibility of arriving at the infernal regions: but we are not taught, that it was a punishment allotted to any of the ghosts, to be thus plunged in it's waves; nor that this circumstance was the cause of the ceaseless lamentations which echoed around it's banks.

What Spenser has invented, and added to antient tradition, concerning Cocytus, exhibits a fine image. He feigns, that when Sir Guyon came to this river,

— — He clomb up to the bank,
And looking downe, saw many damned wights
In those sad waves; which direfull deadly stanke,
Plunged continually of cruel sprights,
That with their piteous cries, and yelling shrights,
They made the further shore resounden wide.

B. ii. c. xii. f. xlvii.

They in that place him GENIUS do call:
Not that cœlestial powre, to whom the care
Of life and generation over all
That lives, pertaines in charge particular,
Who wondrous thinges concerning our welfare,
And strange phantomes does let us oft foresee.

xlviii.

xlviii.

Therefore a God him sage antiquity
Did wisely make, and good Agdistes call,
But this same was to that quite contrary,
The foe of life, that good envies to all,
That secretly doth us procure to fall
Through guilefull semblaunts which he makes us see.

These lines may be farther illustrated, as they are probably drawn, from the following passage in *Natalis Comes.*

" *Dictus est autem* GENIUS, *ut placuit latinis, a gignendo, vel quia nobiscum gignatur, vel quia illi procreandorum cura divinitus commissa putaretur. Hic creditur nobis clam nunc suadens, nunc dissuadens, universam vitam nostram gubernare....... Nam existimantur Genii Dæmones rerum, quas voluerint nobis persuadere, spectra et imagines sibi tanquam in speculo imprimere, quodcunque illis facillimum sit. In quæ spectra cum anima nostra clam respexerit, illa sibi veniunt in mentem, quæ si ratione perpendantur, tum recta fit animi deliberatio: at siquis posthabita ratione, malorum spectrorum et visorum ductu feratur, ille in multos errores incurrat necesse est, si spectra fuerint præcipue a malignis dæmonibus oblata.**" That the first Genius here mentioned was likewise called

* 4. 3.

AGDISTES,

(83)

AGDISTES, we learn from the fame author. " *Quem poftea* Agdiftem *appellarunt.* * "

The ceremony of offering flowers and wine to the Genius expreffed in thefe lines,

> With diverfe flowres he daintily was deckt,
> And ftrowed round about, and by his fide
> A mighty mazer bowle of wine was fett,
> As if it had to him been facrifide. ft. 49.

Is found in Horace,

> — — *piabant*
> *Floribus et vino* GENIUM *memorem brevis ævi* †.

The GENIUS fpoken of in the following ftanzas, feems to be that which is reprefented in the PICTURE of the fophift Cebes.

> And double gates it had, which open'd wide,
> By which both in and out men moten pafs;
> Th' one faire and frefhe, the other old and dride:
> OLD GENIUS the porter of them was,
> OLD GENIUS, the which a double nature has.
> 3. 6. 31.

xxxii.

> He letteth in, he letteth out to wend,
> All that to come into the world defire:
> A thoufand thoufand naked babes atteud

* Ibid. † Epift. 2. b. 2. v. 143.

M 2 About

About him day and night, which doe require,
That he with fleshlie weedes would them attire.

" Ὁρᾷς, ἐφη, τον περιβολον τύτον; Ὁρωμεν. Τύτο πρῶτον δει
ειδεναι ὑμας, ὁτι καλειται ὁ τοπΘ- ύlΘ·, ΒΙΟΣ. Και ὁ οχλΘ·
ὁ πολυς, ὁ παρα την πυλην εφεςως, οἱ μελλονlες εισπορευεσθαι
εις τον βιον, ύlοι εισιν. Ο δε ΓΕΡΩΝ, ὁ ανω ἑςηκως, εχων χαρ-
lην τινα εν τη χειρι, και τη ἑlερα ὡσπερ δεικνυων τι, ύlΘ· ΔΑΙ-
ΜΩΝ καλειται. Προσlαllει δε τοις εισπορευομενοις τι δει αὐlυς
ποιειν, &c." " Cernitis, inquit, septum hoc? Cernimus.
Hoc primùm vobis tenendum est, locum hanc appellari vitam ; et magnam multitudinem, quæ portæ assistit, eos esse
qui in vitam venturi sunt. Senex is qui superne stat, char-
tam quamdam una manu tenens, altera vero quiddam quasi
monstrans, Genius dicitur. Mandat autem ingredientibus,
quid eis, ubi in vitam venerint, faciendum sit."

THE THIRD BOOKE OF THE FAERIE QUEENE;
CONTAINING THE LEGEND OF BRITOMARTIS, OR
OF CHASTITY.

BRITOMARTIS, among the Cretans, was another
name for Diana, the goddess of Chastity; and in this
book, Spenser's Britomartis is represented as the patroness of Chastity. I think she is so called in Claudian. It is not improbable, as our author has copied
the greatest part of the second Canto of this book
from the Ceiris of Virgil, that he found, from
the

the same poem, that Britomartis was a name for Diana, viz.

Dyctinnam dixere tuo *de nomine Lunam* *.

She was a Cretan nymph, and the daughter of Jupiter and Charme, whom Virgil has introduced, in his *Ceiris*, as the nurse of Scylla, and from whom our author has copied his Glauce, Britomart's nurse, in the Canto mentioned above. She was called Dictynna, because she invented nets for hunting, which being also one of Diana's names, Britomartis and Diana were looked upon as the same. Callimachus speaks of her as one of the nymphs of Diana's train, but adds, that she was called by the Cydonians, Dictynna. He has left the history of Britomartis in his hymn to Diana.

Εξοχα δ' αλλαων Γορτυνιδα φιλαο νυμφην
Ελλοφονον ΒΡΙΤΟΜΑΡΤΙΝ, ευσκοπον· ης ποτε Μινως
Πτοιηθεις υπ' ερωτι κατεδραμεν ουρεα Κρητης.
Η δ' οτε μεν λασιησιν υπο δρυσι κρυπτετο νυμφη,
Αλλοτε δ' ειαμενησιν. Ο δ' εννεα μηνας εφοιτα
Παιπαλα τε, κρημνους τε· κ̣ ουκ ανεπαυσε διωκτυν,
Μεσφ' οτε μαρπτομενη και δη σχεδον ηλατο ποντον
Πρηονος εξ υπατοιο, κ̣ ενθορεν εις αλιηων
Δικτυα, τα σφ' εσαωσεν. Οθεν μετεπειτα Κυδωνες

Ver. 305.

Νυμφαν

Νυμφαν μεν ΔΙΚΤΥΝΑΝ· οῤ@· δ' ὁθεν ηλαῖο νυμφη
Δικ]αιον καλεϗσιν· αναϛησανῖο δε ϐωμϗς,
Ιερα δε ῥεζϗσι *. ⸺ ⸺

*Præcipue autem inter alias omnes Gortynida amafti Nympham,
Cervarum Venatricem,* Britomartin, *Jaculatricem; cujus
olim Minos
Amore perculfus, peavagatus eft montes Cretæ.
Illa vero alias quidem hirtis fub quercubus latitabat Nympha,
Alias autem in locis uliginofis. At ipfe novem menfes per-
curvebat
Loca prærupta, et pendentes fcopulos: nec intermifit infec-
tationem,
Donec apprehenfa ferme Nympha infiliit in mare
Ab alto vertice: infiliit autem in pifcatorum
Retia, quæ ipfam confervarunt: hinc deinceps Cydones
Nympham ipfam, Dictynnam; montem vero, unde defiliit
Nympha,
Dictæum appellitant: excitatifque ibi facris
Sacra etiam faciunt.* ⸺ ⸺ ⸺

Upon the word Βριτομαῤτις, fays the fcholiaft, ΒΡΙΤΟ-
ΜΑΡΤΙΣ ονομα το κυριον της νυμφης· αφ' ἡς κ̓ ἡ ΑΡΤΕΜΙΣ εν
Κρητη ΒΡΙΤΟΜΑΡΤΙΣ τιμᾶλαι, ὡς Διογενιαν@·. And Soli-

---

* Ύμν@· εις Αῤτ. v. 189. We read nearly the fame account of this
nymph in the ΜΕΤΑΜΟΡΦΩΣΕΙΣ of Antoninus Liberalis, Fab. 40.
p. 50. Bafil. 1568.

nus

nus speaks to the same effect. " *Cretes Dianam religiosissime venerantur*, Βριτομαρτιν *gentiliter nominantes*; *quod sermone nostro sonat virginem dulcem* ‡." But although Spenser in Britomartis had some reference to *Diana*, yet at the same time he intended to denote by that name the *martial* BRITONESSE.

The reader is desired to take notice, that the passage which Spenser has copied from the *Ceiris* of Virgil, begins at this verse of that poem,

Quam simul Ogygii Phænicis filia CHARME, * —

And ends at,

Despue ter, virgo : numero deus impare gaudet †.

B. ii. c. ix. f. xxii.

He is describing the *Castle* of ALMA.

The frame thereof seem'd partly circulare,
And part triangulare, &c.

The philosophy of this abstruse stanza, is explained in a learned epistle of Sir Kenelm Digby §, addressed

‡ Polyhist. c. 17.   * Ver. 223.   † Ver. 373.
§ First printed in a single pamphlet. viz. Observations on xxii. stanza, &c. Lond. 1644. 8vo. It is also published in *Scrinia Sacra*, 4to. pag. 244. London, 1654.

to

to Sir Edward Stradling. It is partly formed on the syftem of Plato, who was a great favorite of thofe writers, whom Spenfer chiefly ftudied and copied, the Italian poets, particularly Petrarch. The fixth canto of the third book, efpecially the fecond, and the thirty-fecond ftanza, explained above, together with his *Hymnes of heavenly Love* and *heavenly Beauty*, are evident proofs of our author's attachment to the Platonic fchool.

The notions of our author's friend, Sir Philip Sydney, who, with many others of that age, had a ftrong Platonic caft, perhaps contributed not a little to fix Spenfer's choice on the fubject of the *Hymnes* juft mentioned. Take his own words in the *Defence of Poefie*. "That lyrical kind of fongs and fonnets — which — "how well it might be employed, and with how hea- "venly fruits both in publicke and private, in finging "the praifes of the IMMORTAL BEAUTY*."

B. iii. c. vi. f. xxx.

He fpeaks of the *Garden* of Adonis.

> In that fame garden all the goodly flowres
> Wherewith dame Nature doth her beautifie,
> Are fetcht: there is the firft feminarie
> Of all things that are born to live and die.

* Ad Calc. Pembroke's Arcadia, pag. 564. Edit. up fupr.

In

In his particular description of this garden, the general idea of which is founded in antient story, he perhaps had an eye to that part of the fable of Adonis, in which he is supposed to represent the sun, which quickens the growth of all things. Thus Orpheus in his Hymn to Adonis.

Ευβελι, πολυμορφε, τροφη παντων αριδηλε,
Κυρη και κορε, συ πασι θαλ⊙· αιεν, Αδωνι,
Σβεννυμενε, λαμπωντε καλαις εν κυκλασιν ωραις.

Prudens, multiformis, pabulum omnibus præclarum,
Puella et puer, tu omnibus germen, Adoni,
Extincte, fulgensque in pulchris redeuntibus horis.

Others represent him as the seed of wheat. Thus the scholiasts on Theocritus. " Τετο το λεγομενον, τοιετον εςιν αληθως· Ότι ὁ Αδωνις, ητεν ὁ σιτ⊙· ὁ σπειρομεν⊙·, εξ μηνας εν τη γη ποιει ὑπο της σπορας, κὴ εξ μηνας εχει αυτον ἡ Αφροδιτη, τετεςιν, ἡ ευκρασια τε αερος, κὴ εκτοτε λαμβανεσον αυτον οι ανθρωποι*." " *Hoc revera ita se habet: scilicet quod Adonis est Frumentum satum; quod sex menses sub terra degit, et sex menses eum habet Venus; nimirum aeris temperies, et postea a messoribus colligitur.*" Orpheus, in the same hymn, calls the body of Adonis,

——— ——— Δεμας ωριοκαρπον.
——— ——— — *Corpus frugiferum.*

* Ad Idyll. 3. v. 48.

He has placed Cupid and Pſyche in this garden, where they live together in,

—— Stedfaſt love, and happy ſtate.   ſt. 50.

But Apuleius repreſents this happy ſtate of Cupid and Pſyche, to have commenced after their reception into heaven. However their offspring *Pleaſure* is authoriſed by Apuleius. " *Sic ecce* Pſyche *venit in manum* Cupidinis; *et naſcitur illis maturo partu filia quam* VOLUPTATEM *nominamus* *." He has made *Pleaſure* the daughter of Cupid in another poem. Speaking to that deity.

> There with thy daughter *Pleaſure* they do play
> Their hurtleſſe ſports †. — — —
>
>   B. iii. c. xi. ſ. xlvii.

Of the ſtatue of Cupid.

> — Wings it had with ſundrie colours dight,
> More ſundrie colours than the proud pavone
> Bears in his boaſted fan, or Iris bright,
> When her diſcolour'd bow ſhe ſpreads thro' heaven bright.

Cupid was repreſented by the antients with particoloured wings, as we learn, among others, from the following paſſage of an epigram aſcribed to Virgil.

* Metam. l. 6.   † HYMNE to Love.

Marmoreuſque

Marmoreusque tibi DIVERSICOLORIBUS *alis*
 In morem picta stabit Amor *pharetra**.

But this splendid plumage was probably supplied by Spenser's imagination; or from that fund of brilliant imagery, the italian poets. In the *Pastorals*, MARCH, he draws Cupid after the same manner.

> With that sprung forth a naked swaine,
> With spotted wings like peacocke's traine.

Thus also Cupid. in the next canto, st. 23.

> And clapt on high his coloured winges twaine.

In *Muipotmos* his wings are compared with those of a butterfly.

> Bears in his wings so manie a changefull token.

In the comparison of the peacock and the rainbow, as they occur together, he probably imitated Tasso.

> *Ne 'l superbo* Pavon *si vago in monstra*
> *Spiega la pompa de l'* occhiute piume:
> *Ne l'* Iride *si bella indora, e inostra*
> *Il curvo grembo e rugiadoso lumè* †.

* Virgil. Catalect. Burman. edit. vol. 4. pag. 143. AD VENEREM.
† Gier. Liberat. c. 16. s. 24.

> The jolly *Peacock* spreads not half so fair
> The *eyed feathers* of his pompous train;
> Nor so bends golden *Iris* in the air
> Her twenty-colour'd bow thro' clouds of rain.
>
> Fairfax.

He has again joined these two comparisons. Speaking of a butterfly's wings, as before.

> Not half so many sundrie colours are
> In Iris bowe, — — —
> Nor Juno's bird, in her eye-spotted traine,
> So many goodlie colours doth containe*.

Where *eye-spotted traine* is plainly the *occhiute piume* of the italian poet. Shakespeare calls the peacock

> ——— The *eye-train'd* Bird †.

Chaucer, in one of his figures of Cupid, supposes that his wings were adorned with shining feathers.

> And *Angelike* his wingis sawe I sprede ‡.
>
> B. iii. c. xii. s. vii.

> And everie wood and every valley wide
> He fill'd with Hylas' name; the nymphes eke Hylas cride.

* Muipotmos. † Tam. Shrew. A. 4. sc. 13. ‡ Leg. of G. Wom. v. 236.

Moft of the antient writers, who relate the hiftory of Hylas, mention the circumftance of Hylas's name being often re-echoed by the hills, &c. when it was fo loudly and frequently called upon by Hercules. But I do not recollect that any of them reprefent the nymphs as repeating his name. With regard to the former particular, Antoninus Liberalis has given us an explication of it, not generally known, from the loft ΕΤΕΡΟΙΟΥΜΕΝΩΝ, or *Transformations*, of Nicander. " Hercules, fays he, having made the hills and forefts tremble, by calling *Hylas* fo mightily; the nymphs who had fnatched him away, fearing left the enraged lover fhould at laft difcover Hylas in their fountain, transformed him into Echo, who anfwered *Hylas* to every call of Hercules." This folution throws a new light on the circumftance of Hylas's name being fo often echoed back, and accounts for it being fo particularly and uniformly infifted on by Propertius*, Virgil †, and Valerius Flaccus §. And that this was a common tradition of antiquity, though not commonly recorded, is ftill further manifefted by what Antoninus continues to relate from the fame Nicander. " The inhabitants to this day facrifice to Hylas on the banks of his foun-

* De Raptu Hylæ, El. 1. 20. † Eclog. 6. v. 44.
§ Argon. l. 7. 593.

tain;

tain; in which ceremony the prieſt calls out Hylas thrice, and is anſwered *Hylas* by Echo thrice.*"

The diſappointment and diſtreſs of Hercules, after he had loſt his favorite Hylas, is well deſcribed by Valerius Flaccus †; particularly the circumſtance of the night coming on, and adding to his fears, is beautifully touched.

*— — Varios hinc excitat æſtus
Nube mali percuſſus amor; quibus hæſerit oris,
Quis tales impune moras, caſuſve laborve,
Attulerit*; denſam interea deſcendere noctem
Jam majore metu; *tum vero et pallor et amens
Cum piceo ſudore rigor.* — —

And the artifice by which Hylas is decoyed to the fountain, is a pretty poetical fiction ‡. It is remark-

---

* There is good reaſon to conclude, that this book of Antoninus, which conſiſts of various little hiſtories, was collected, rather than compoſed, by it's author. Many of the ſtories ſeem to be literally tranſcribed from the reſpective mythologiſts who are referred to in each. This is highly probable, as the greek of ſome of the ſtories is extremely pure, ſuch as could not well be written by a roman, and eſpecially one who lived in the decline of the empire. There is likewiſe a great variety of ſtyles in the different narrations, and yet a ſameneſs of ſtyle in thoſe which bear the name of the ſame author. Thus this compiler is more valuable than is imagined, as he has preſerved to us the fragments of many famous authors, all whoſe works are ſuppoſed to be entirely loſt.

† Argon. 3. 565. ſeq.   ‡ Ibid. v. 545.

able,

able, that Scaliger, who, in general, prefers Flaccus to his original Apollonius, should deliver this opinion upon the similies of both poets, concerning the anguish felt by Hercules on the loss of Hylas. " *Hæc quidem* [Flacci] *sonora magis; plus tamen arrident Græca* *." This indeed is a high concession from a critic, who has indiscriminately declared himself a professed enemy to the more antient and simple grecian poets. In his Comparison of Homer with Virgil, one would suspect, that he had received some personal affront from the former; and by producing a short specimen of his manner, I will give the reader an opportunity of determining, whether the censures which Scaliger casts upon the father of poetry in the course of this comparison, are the effect of taste and judgement, or of caprice and ignorance. He informs us, that Homer is little better than a common cryer, as different from Virgil, as a grave and prudent matron from a weak giddy girl; he tells scandalous lies; his syrens in the Odyssey sing such a wretched song, as would hardly tempt his [Scaliger's] cook to dance; his epithets are mostly frigid, childish, and foolish; some of his lines are written by a school-boy, and some are as barbarous as the Polypheme he describes;

* Poet. b. 5. l. 6.

he puts a bawdy word into the mouth of Juno, importing the act of generation; he has no notion of boar-hunting; he has most improperly placed a blacksmith's shop in heaven; he describes the fall of a poplar-tree with as little skill as a carpenter would shew in felling it; his Nestor is a mere babbler in the first and seventh Iliad, in the eleventh quite wearies the reader, and in the twenty-third turns downright driveller; he wrote over a bottle, &c. &c *. The truth is, that Scaliger had no notion of simple and genuine beauty; nor had ever considered the manners and customs which prevailed in the early times.

B. iv. c. x. f. xlvii.

To Venus.

Great God, &c.

The poet prepares the reader for this appellation *God*, applied to Venus. st. 41.

> But for they say, she has both kinds in one,
> Both male and female, both under one name:
> She sire and mother is herself alone,
> Begets and eke conceives, ne needeth other none.

He has also followed the same notion in *Colin Clouts Come Home Again*.

* Ibid. passim.

For

For Venus selfe doth solely couples seeme,
Both male and female through commixture joyn'd.

Thus he has made *Envy* male, 1. 4. 30. and female, 5. 12. 29.

B. v. c. i. s. xii.

But when she parted thence she left her groome
An yron man, which did on her attend,
Alwayes to execute her stedfast doome,
And willed him with Arthegall to wend,
And do whatever things he did intend:
His name was TALUS, made of iron mould,
Immoveable, resistless, without end;
Who in his hand an iron flail did hold,
With which he thresht out falsehood, and did truth unfold.

The character of executing justice, here attributed to TALUS, is agreeable to that which he bears in antient story; nor has Spenser greatly varied from antiquity in the make of this wonderful man; for he is there said to be formed of brass, and by our author of iron. Plato gives the following account of him.

" Νομοφυλακι γαρ αυτω [Ραδαμανθω] εχρητο ὁ Μινως κατα αστυ· τα δε κατα την αλλην Κρητην τω ΤΑΛΩ. Ο γαρ ΤΑΛΩΣ τρις περιηει τε ενιαυτε κατα τας κωμας, φυλαττων τες νομες εν αυταις εν χαλκοις

χαλκοις γραμμαΐειοις εχων γεγραμμενυς· ὁθεν ΧΑΛΚΟΥΣ εκληθη *." Utebatur autem Minos hoc legum fuarum cuftode apud urbem; in cæteris vero Cretæ partibus Talo. Et profecto Talus ter in anno vicos circuibat, legibus tuendis intentus in illis; quas habebat in æneis tabulis infcriptas; unde nuncupatus eft Talus." As to the circumſtance of Talus traverſing the iſle of Crete, it exactly correſponds with what Spenſer ſays afterwards of his iron man, who did the ſame in Ierne.

And that ſame yron man, which could reveale
All hidden crimes, thro' all that realme he ſent,
To ſearch out thoſe that us'd to rob and ſteale,
Or did rebell 'gainſt lawfull government.

6. 12. 26.

Plato has told us, that TALUS was denominated *brazen*, on account of his carrying the laws about him, written in brazen tables; but Apollonius informs us, that he was actually made of braſs, and invulnerable.

Αλλ' ἤτοι το μεν αλλο δεμας, κ̀ γυια, τέτυκίο
Χαλκει©·, κ̀ αρρηκίος· υπαι δε ὁι εσκε τενοντος
Συριγξ αιματοεσσα κατα σφυρον· αιταρ ὁ τηνγε
Λεπτος υμην ζωης εχε πειρατα κ̀ θανατοιο *.

* In Minoe. Plat. op. edit. Serran. pag. 230. vol. 1.

† Αργον. b. 4. v. 1645. Ibycus, quoted by Athenæus, relates that Talus was beloved by Rhadamanthus. lib. 13. pag. 603. Ed. Ludg. 1657. fol.

Sed

*Sed is cum cætero corpore et membris esset
Æneus, et invulnerabilis, tamen sub tenonte habebat
In malleolo turgentem sanguine venam, quam tenuis
Continebat tunicula, et vitæ præstabat mortisque con-
finium.*

Apollonius likewise takes notice of his circuiting Crete three times a year.

Τρις περι χαλκειοις Κρητην ποσι δινευοντα *.

Ter in anno Cretam æneis obeuntem pedibus.

Apollodorus will farther illustrate this matter. " Ενθεν αναχθεντες [Αργοναυται] κωλυονται Κρητη προσισχειν υπο ΤΑΛΩ· τυτον οι μεν τυ χαλκυ γενυς ειναι λεγυσιν· οι δε υπο Ηφαιστυ Μινω δοθηναι· ος ην ΧΑΛΚΟΥΣ ΑΝΗΡ· οιδε Ταυρον αυτον λεγουσιν. Ειχε δε φλεβα μιαν απο αυχενος κατατεινυσαν αχρι σφυρων· κατα δε το δερμα της φλεβος ηλος διηριστο χαλκους. Ουτ⊙· ο ΤΑΛΩΣ τρις εκαστης ημερας την νησον περιτροχαζων ετηρει †." "*Exinde navigantes prohibentur quo minus Cretæ appellerent a Talo; hunc quidem ænei generis hominum esse dicunt; illi a Vulcano Minoi traditum fuisse: erat autem homo aheneus: sunt autem qui eum Taurum nominant. Habebat vero venam unam a cervice usque ad crura protensam; in tunicula vero venæ æneus infigebatur clavus. Talus*

* Ibid. v. 1646.   † Bibliothec. b. 1. c. 26.

iste

iste ter unoquoque die insulam percurrens eam contuebatur." This marvellous swiftness of Talus is likewise referred to by our author.

> His yron page, who him pursewd so light,
> As that it seem'd above the ground he went,
> For he was swift as swallow in her flight. 5. 1. 20.

And is alluded to by Catullus, in his Ode to Camerius, where he tells him that he should not be able to pursue him,

> *Non* CUSTOS *si ego fingar illé* CRETUM *.

Orpheus, or rather † Onomacritus, calls TALUS, in his Argonautics,

Χαλκειον τριγιγαντα ‡. — — —

" The *brazen triple-giant.*"

The circumstance of the iron flail is added from our author's imagination.

* Car. 56.

† Who lived in the time of the Pisistratic tyranny, about Olymp. 60. For a proof that the Argonautics, attributed to Orpheus, are the work of Onomacritus, see Voss. de Poet. Græc. c. 2. and c. 4. Olai Borrichii Dissert. de Poet. Græc. Dissert. 1. par. 17. See also Rhunken. Epist. Crit. ii. pag. 69. And Fulvius Ursinus, on Virgil's Imitations; Leovardiæ, 1747. pag. 38. apud Eclog. 3.

‡ Αργον. v. 1348.

B. V.

B. v. c. viii. f. xlvii.

Like raging Ino when with knife in hand
She threw her hufband's murder'd infant out.

Ovid reports, *Met.* iv. 528. that Ino threw herfelf, together with her fon Melicerta, from the fummit of a rock into the fea. Others relate that fhe murdered Melicerta, and afterwards leaped into the fea. It is difficult to fix upon Spenfer's precife meaning in thefe verfes.

Ibid.

Or as that madding mother, 'mongft the rout
Of Bacchus' priefts, her own deare flefh did teare.

The *Madding Mother* is AGAVE. Her fon Pentheus being, of a very temperate difpofition, and confequently averfe to the rites of Bacchus, fhe, together with the reft of the Mænades, tore him in pieces, in the midft of the Bacchanalia.

Mr. Upton*, inftead of,

— — Her *owne* dear flefh did teare,

would read, her SON's *dear flefh*. But furely the poet, and with no great impropriety of expreffion, might mean her *Son*'s flefh, by her *owne* flefh.

* Letter to G. Weft.

B. v.

B. v. c. x. f. x.

Orthrus, begotten by great Typhaon,
And fowle Echidna, — —

who guarded the purple oxen of Geryon.

I wonder that Spenser should in this place have omitted the mention of a seven-headed dragon, who, together with Orthrus, was stationed to guard these oxen, and was likewise the offspring of Typhaon and Echidna. A dragon was too tempting a circumstance to be omitted.

B. iv. c. xi. f. xiii.

He is giving a catalogue of the sea-gods; among the rest is Astræus,

— — that did shame
Himselfe with incest of his kin unkend.

Natalis Comes thus relates the story of Astræus. " *Astræus, qui per inscitiam congressus cum Alcippe sorore, sequenti die cognita affinitate ex annulo, mærore captus se in fluvium præcipitavit, qui prius dictus est Astræus ab ipso, &c* *." I think he is mentioned in Ælian. Of these afterwards, f. 17.

* 2. 8.

But

But why do I their names feeke to reherfe,
Which all the world have with their iffue fill'd?
How can they all in this fo narrow verfe
Contained be, &c.

Natalis Comes, having finifhed his catalogue of thefe divinities, adds, " *Ut alios infinitos prope prætermittam; nam plures quam octoginta me legiffe memini.*" Spenfer apparently took his catalogue from this mythologift.

Natalis Comes was then juft publifhed, and, I fuppofe, a popular book.

B. iv. c. xi. f. xix.

— — — So wife is Nereus old,
And fo well fkill'd: nathleffe he takes great joy
Oft-times among the wanton nymphes to fport and toy.

Of the juftice and prophetical power of Nereus, teftimonies are obvious. The latter part of his character may be illuftrated from thefe verfes of Orpheus[*].

Πεντηκοντα ΚΟΡΑΙΣΙΝ ΑΓΑΛΛΟΜΕΝΟΣ κατα κυμα
Καλλιτεκνοισι χοροις, Νερευ. ———

*Quinquaginta puellis lætate in fluctibus,
Elegantibus choris, Nereu.*

[*] Hymn.

B. vi.

B. vi. c. x. f. xxii.

Of the Graces.

They are the daughters of fky-ruling Jove,
By him begot of fair Eurynome.

Milton, in *L'Allegro*, reprefents the Graces as the offspring of Venus and Bacchus. This mythology, as an ingenious critic on that paffage obferves, fuits the nature of Milton's fubject; but I cannot be perfuaded, that fuch a licence is allowable on any occafion.

The mention of Eurynome, in this ftanza, puts me in mind of another paffage in Milton, where the fame goddefs is alfo mentioned.

And fabled how the ferpent, whom they call'd
Ophion, with *Eurynome*, the wide
Encroaching Eve, perhaps, had firft the rule
Of high Olympus [*].

Which, as the learned Dr. Newton, and others, obferve, is copied from thefe verfes of Apollonius:

Ηειδεν δ' ως πρωτον Οφιων, Ευρυνομη τε
Ωκεανις, νιφοεντος εχον κρατ⊙· Ουλυμποιο [†].

Et cecinit ut in principio Ophion, Eurynomeque Oceanis, nivofi tenuerint verticem Olympi.

[*] Parad. Loft. b. x. v. 530. [†] Αργον. b. i. v. 496.

What

What I would further obferve here, is, that Apollonius, as well as Milton, has hinted, that Ophion was of the *serpent* race. This will appear from confidering the lines juft preceding. Orpheus begins his fong with the creation of things. After mentioning the fun and moon, mountains and rivers, he fpeaks of the creation of ferpents.

Ουρεα τ' ως ανετειλε, κ) ως ποταμοι κελαδοντες
Αυτησι Νυμφησι, κ) ΕΡΠΕΤΑ παντ' εγενοντο *.

*Quomodo orti funt montes, et refonantes fluvii
Cum ipfis nymphis, et quomodo omnia reptilia concreverint.*

And in the next line, from thofe ΕΡΠΕΤΑ, or *ferpents*, he directly paffes on to Ophion.

Ηειδεν δ' ως πρωτον ΟΦΙΩΝ, &c.

Thus there is a clofer connection, and an eafier tranfition, in the context of the greek poet, than appears at firft fight.

Spenfer alludes to this fong of Orpheus, and the occafion on which it was fung, more than once.

* Αργον. b. i. v. 501.

Such one was Orpheus, that when ſtrife was grown
Amongſt thoſe famous impes of greece, did take
His ſilver harp in hand, and ſhortly friends them make.

4. 2. 1.

And in Sonnet 44.

When thoſe renowned noble peres of greece
Through ſtubborn pride among themſelves did jar,
Forgetful of the famous golden fleece,
Then Orpheus with his harp their ſtrife did bar.

Scaliger greatly cenſures the ſubject of this ſong in Apollonius, and prefers to it, the argument of the ſong of Orpheus, in Valerius Flaccus. " *Longe enim aptius* [Orpheus] *canit apud* Flaccum, *Minyas, et Phryxum et Athamantem, quam apud Apollonium terræ cœlique creationem. Quid enim Viris Militaribus cum Philoſophorum Umbris**?" But by this piece of criticiſm, Scaliger, not leſs remarkably than in his notions about Homer, has betrayed his ignorance of the nature of antient poetry, and of the character of Orpheus. " In the early ages
" of the grecian ſtate, the wild and barbarous inha-
" bitants wanted the aſſiſtance of the Muſes to ſoften
" and tame them. They ſtood in need of being
" impreſſed with an awe of ſuperior and irreſiſtible

* Poet. b. 5. c. 6.

" powers,

"powers, and a liking to social life. They wanted a mythology to lead them by fear and dread, the only holds to be taken of a rude multitude, into a feeling of natural causes, and their influence upon our lives and actions. The wise and good among the antients saw this necessity and supplied it; the oldest of the inspired train were the Pii Vates, et Phœbo digna locuti: they had religion for their theme, and the service of mankind for their song *." And in another place the same author observes, that all the poems of Orpheus were " philosophical, pro- phetical, and religious †." The conduct therefore of Apollonius was perfectly just, in attributing a song to Orpheus, the subject of which was philosophy and religion. And it was for the same reason that ‡ Onomacritus, many years before Apollonius, represented Orpheus singing the origin of the gods, and the creation of things, in his contest with Chiron.

But the propriety of the subject of this song in Apollonius, is easily to be defended, without considering the character of Orpheus. The occasion of the song was a general quarrel among the argonauts, whom Orpheus endeavours to pacify with the united powers of

* Blackwall's Enquiry into the life, &c. of Homer, s. vi.
† S. vii.   ‡ Argon. v. 419.

P 2   music

music and verse. On which account, says the scholiast, "Την πρώτην συγχυσιν των ϛοιχειων ἀδειν βουλεῖαι, ὡς εκ τινῶ- φιλονεικιας το ιδιον εκαϛον μεῖεσχεν, κὶ ταξιν ελαβεν. Οικεια δε κὶ τοις ὑποκειμενοις πραῖμασιν ἡ ὠδη. Ὁτι εϛι της μαχης παυσασθαι, κὶ εις την οικειαν διαθεσιν επανιεναι." To this we may add, that a song whose subject is also religious, and which asserts the right Jupiter to the possession of Olympus, was here not only proper, but even expedient, as one of the argonauts had but just before blasphemed Jupiter*. Nor were the auditors of this song altogether of so mean a condition as Scaliger insinuates. He terms them VIRI MILITARES; but it is to be remembered that they were PRINCES and DEMIGODS.

But whether the subject of the song of Orpheus in Apollonius be blameable or not, it has one essential circumstance, which indisputably gives it a superiority to that of Orpheus in Valerius Flaccus; I mean the design of it, which was to repress the vehemence of the passions: a design, at once so agreeable to the peculiar character of Orpheus, and so expressive of the influence of music. In the latin poet, Orpheus sings upon no occasion, and to no end, unless it be to that general one of entertainment, and of making the night pass more pleasantly,

* L. i. v. 466.

Thracius

Thracius hic NOCTEM *dulci teſtudine vates*
EXTRAHIT *. — — —

Milton in the following verſes alludes both to Apollonius and Onomacritus, in their reſpective ſongs of Orpheus.

Tunc de more ſedens feſta ad convivia vates
Æſculea intonſos redimitus ab arbore crines,
Heroumque actus, imitandaque geſta canebat;
Et Chaos, et poſiti late fundamina mundi;
Reptanteſque deos, et alentes numina glandes;
Et nondum Ætneo quæſitum fulmen ab antro.
Denique quid vobis modulamen inane juvabit,
Verborum ſenſuſque vacans, numerique loquacis?
Silveſtres decet iſte choros, non Orphea, *cantus;*
Qui tenuit fluvios, et quercubus addidit aures,
Carmine, non cithara §. — — —

Silius Italicus alludes to the conteſt of Chiron with Orpheus, as related by Onomacritus. In deſcribing the miraculous force of the muſic of Orpheus, he has plainly tranſlated from the greek poet; particularly in this circumſtance.

Οιωνοι τ' εκυκλευΐο βοαυλια Κενΐαυροιο
Ταρσοις κεκμηωσιν, εης δ' ελαθονΐο καλιης. ‡.

* Argon. b. 1. v. 277.   § Ad Patrem. v. 44.   ‡ 436.

Aveſque

Avesque circumdederunt stabula Centauri,
Pennis defessis, suique oblitæ erant nidi.

The verses of Silius Italicus are these.

Immemor et dulcis nidi, positoque volatu,
Non mota volueris captiva pependit in æthra*.

The latin poet has however omitted to describe the manner in which Chiron was affected, at seeing the wonderful effect of Orpheus's music on the trees, mountains, rivers, beasts, &c. His astonishment on that occasion is thus characteristically and beautifully painted by Onomacritus.

Αὐταρ ορων Κενταυρος εθαμβεε, χειρ' επι καρπω
Πυκνον επισσειων· ϋδας δ'ηρασσεν οπλησιν †.

Sed videns hæc Centaurus obstupuit; manum super
volam
Valde feriens, terramque pulsavit unguibus.

I fear I have digressed too far already. But an imitation of Milton from his favorite Apollonius having been produced in this remark, I hope I shall be pardoned for taking so fair an opportunity of introducing another. Milton thus describes Adam's hair,

* B. II. v. 467. † Αργον. 438.
— Hyacinthine

(111)

— — — Hyacinthine locks
Round from his parted forelock manly hung
CLUSTRING *.

The circumstance of the hair hanging like bunches of grapes, has been justly admired: but it is literally translated from this description of Apollo's hair in Apollonius.

—— Κρυσεοι δε παρειαων εκατερθε
Πλοχμοι ΒΟΤΡΥΟΕΝΤΕΣ επερρωοντο κιοντι †.

— Aurei ab utraque gena
Cincinni racemantes assultabant eunti.*

The word Βοτρυοεντες could hardly have been rendered into english by any other word than *clustring*. But it must not be omitted here, that we find the same metaphor in a little poem on the statue of Homer, in the *Anthologia*.

Αυχενι μεν κυπτοντι γερων επεσυρετο ΒΟΤΡΥΣ
ΚΑΙΤΗΣ, εισοπισω πεφορημεν⊕ ‡. —

Cervice quidem inclinata senex [canus] trahebatur
   racemus
Comæ, in tergum delatus. — —

* Par. L. b. 4. v. 301.
† Αργον. l. 2. v. 678.
‡ Henr. Steph. fol. 1566. βιβ. πεμπτ. pag. 394. Εις ΟΜΗΡΟΝ. Carm. 16.

B. vii.

B. vii. c. vi. f. iii.

Spenser here makes Hecate the daughter of the Titans. Authors differ about the parentage of Hecate. Onomacritus calls her,

Ταρταρόπαις Εκάτη *. — — —

Tartari filia Hecate. — —

The Titans were indeed thrown into Tartarus; but it could not be concluded from thence that the Titans were Hecate's parents; although this, I presume, is the best argument our author could have offered for his genealogy. In this stanza Bellona is likewise feigned to be the offspring of the Titans; but Bellona was the sister of Mars, who was son of Jupiter and Juno; or, as Ovid reports, of Juno alone.

A classical reader of the FAIRY QUEEN may discover many more examples which properly belong to this section. But my principal design was to select those allusions, which best shewed how such an invention as Spenser's acted on the fictions of others. Hence it was necessary sometimes to enter into a minute detail of the fables of antiquity, not out of an ostentation of erudition, but that it might appear,

* Αργον. v. 975.

what belonged to the poet, and what to antient story. Those examples which are here omitted, have been collected by the author of *Remarks on Spenser's Poems*, with all the learning and sagacity for which that critic is so remarkable, and which are so peculiarly requisite for such a research.

SECT. IV.

Of Spenser's Stanza, Versification, and Language.

ALTHOUGH Spenser's favorite Chaucer had made use of the *ottava rima* *, or stanza of eight lines; yet it seems probable, that Spenser was principally induced to adopt it, with the addition of one line, from the practice of Ariosto and Tasso, the most fashionable poets of his age. But Spenser, in chusing this stanza, did not sufficiently consider the genius of the english language, which does not easily fall into a frequent repetition of the same termination; a circumstance natural to the italian, which deals largely in identical cadences.

* Chaucer's stanza is not *strictly* so. Betussi in his Life of Boccace, acquaints us, that Boccace was the inventor of of the OTTAVA RIMA, and that the *Theseide* of that author was the first poem in which it was ever applied.

Besides, it is to be remembered, that Tasso and Ariosto did not embarrass themselves with the necessity of finding out so many similar terminations as Spenser. Their *ottava rima* has only three similar endings, alternately rhyming. The two last lines formed a distinct rhyme. But in Spenser, the second rhyme is repeated four times, and the third three *.

This constraint led our author into many absurdities; the most striking and obvious of which seem to be the following.

I. It obliged him to dilate the thing to be expressed, however unimportant, with trifling and tedious circumlocutions, viz.

> Now hath fair Phœbe, with her silver face,
> Thrice seen the shadows of this nether world,
> Sith last I left that honourable place,
> In which her royal presence in enroll'd.
>
> 2. 3. 44.

That is, " it is three months since I left her palace."

II. It necessitated him, when matter failed towards the close of a stanza, to run into a ridiculous redundancy and repetition of words, viz.

---

* See examples of the measures of the Provencial poets, in Petrarch. Spenser forms a compound of many of these.

In

In which was nothing pourtrahed nor wrought,
Nor wrought nor pourtrahed, but easie to be thought.
2. 9. 33.

III. It forced him, that he might make out his complement of rhymes, to introduce a puerile or impertinent idea, viz.

Not that proud towre of Troy, though richly GILT.
2. 9. 45.

Being here laid under the compulsion of producing a consonant word to *spilt* and *built*, which are preceding rhymes, he has mechanically given us an image at once little and improper.

To the difficulty of a stanza so injudiciously chosen, I think we may properly impute the great number of his elleipses, some of which will be pointed out at large in another place; and it may be easily conceived, how that constraint which occasioned superfluity, should at the same time be the cause of omission.

Notwithstanding these inconveniencies flow from Spenser's measure, it must yet be owned, that some advantages arise from it; and we may venture to affirm, that the fullness and significancy of Spenser's descriptions, is often owing to the prolixity of his stanza,

stanza, and the multitude of his rhymes. The discerning reader is desired to consider the following stanza, as an instance of what is here advanced. Guyon is binding FUROR.

> With hundred iron chaines he did him bind
> And hundred knots, which did him sore constraine;
> Yet his great iron teeth he still did grind,
> And grimly gnash, threatening revenge in vaine:
> His burning eyen, whom bloudie strakes did staine,
> Stared full wide, and threw forth sparks of fire;
> And more for ranke despight, than for great paine,
> Shakt his long locks colour'd like copper wire,
> And bit his tawny beard, to shew his raging ire.
>
> 2. 4. 15.

In the subsequent stanza there are some images, which perhaps were produced by a multiplicity of rhymes.

> He all that night, that too long night did passe,
> And now the day out of the ocean-maine
> Began to peep above this earthly masse,
> With pearly dew sprinkling the morning grasse;
> Then up he rose like heavy lump of leade,
> That in his face, as in a looking glasse,
> The signs of anguish one might plainly reade.
>
> 3. 5. 26.

Dryden,

Dryden, I think, somewhere remarks, that rhyme often helped him to a thought; an observation, which, probably, Spenser's experience had likewise supplied him with. Spenser, however, must have found more assistance in this respect, from writing in rhyme, than Dryden, in proportion as his stanza obliged him to a more repeated use of it.

In speaking of Spenser's rhyme, it ought to be remarked, that he often new-spells a word to make it rhyme more precisely.

Take these specimens.

And of her own foule entrailes makes her *meat*,
Meat fit for such a monster's monsterous DIEAT.
6. 12. 31.

Timely to joy, and carry comely *cheare*,
For though this clowd have now me overcast,
Yet do I not of better times DESPEARE.
5. 5. 38.

Though when the term is full ACCOMPLISHID,
Then shall a sparke of fire which hath long while
Bene in his ashes raked up and *hid*. 3. 3. 47.

Then all the rest into their coches CLIM,
And through, &c.
Upon great Neptune's necke they softly *swim*.
3. 4. 42.

— — — — — Mightily *amate*,
As faft as forward earft, now backward to RETRATE.
4. 3. 26.

Shall have that golden girdle for *reward*,
And of, &c.
Shall to the faireft lady be PREFAR'D.   4. 2. 27.

——— ——— Into the hardeft *ftone*,
Such as behind their backes, &c.
Were thrown by Pyrrha, and DEUCALIONE.
5. Introd. 2.

And, to be fhort, we meet with *ycled* for yclad, *darre* for dare, *prejudize* for prejudice, *fam* for fame, *lam* for lamb, *denay* for deny, *pervart* for pervert, *heare* for hair, and numberlefs other inftances of orthography deftroyed for the fake of rhyme. This was a liberty which Chaucer, Gower, and Lydgate frequently made ufe of; and it may not be improper in this place, to exhibit the fentiments of a critic in queen Elizabeth's age upon it. " Now there cannot be in a MAKER
" a fowler fault than to falfifie his accent to ferve his
" cadence; or by untrue orthograghy to wrench his
" words to help his rhyme; for it is a fign that fuch
" a maker is not copious in his own language."—
However he feems afterwards to allow the deviation

---

* The author of the Arte of englifh Poefie. fupr. citat.

from true spelling, in some measure. " It is some-
" what more tollerable to help the rhyme by false
" orthographie, than to leave an unpleasant dissonance
" to the eare, by keeping trewe orthographie and
" losing the rime; as for example, it is better to
" rime *dore* with *restore*, than in his true orthographie
" which is *doore*.—— Such men were in effect the
" most part of all your old rimers, and 'specially
" Gower, who to make up his rime, would for the
" most part write his terminant syllable with false
" orthographie; and many times not sticke to put a
" plaine french word for an english; and so by
" your leave do many of our common rimers at
" this day*."

We find in many passages of our author the orthography violated, when the rhyme without such an expedient would be very exact; thus BITE, when made to rhyme with DELIGHT, is sometimes spelt BIGHT, as if the eye could be satisfied in this case as well as the ear. Instances of this sort occur often in Harrington's Ariosto, and more particularly of the word *said*, which is often occasionally written SED. This practice was continued as far down as the age of Milton.

* B. 2. c. 3.

Besides

Besides what the grim wolf, with privy paw
Daily devours apace, and nothing SED.

Said is thus printed SED in the edition of 1645, that it might appear to rhyme, with greater propriety, to the preceding *spread:* later editors, not knowing the fashion of writing *said,* upon some occasions, SED, altered it to *sed,* which utterly destroyed the sense. The same spelling is found again in the same edition, and for the same reason, in *L'Allegro.*

She was pincht and pull'd she SED,
And he by friers lantern *led**.

* I shall here take occasion to illustrate the lines immediately following.

> Tells how the drudging goblin swet
> To earn his cream-bowl duly set,
> When, &c. - - - - -
> Then lies him down the LUBBAR-FIEND;
> And stretcht out all the chimney's length,
> Baskes at the fire his hairy strength;
> And crop-full out of doors he flings,
> E'er the first cock his mattin rings.

The *Goblin* is Shakespeare's *Robin Goodfellow,* and the tradition about him is found in *Harsenet's Declaration,* &c. quoted above. " And if " that the bowle of curdes and creame were not duly sett out for *Robin* " *Goodfellow,* the frier, and Sifs the dairy-maid, to meet him at, &c. " why then either the pottage, &c." pag. 135. ch. 20.

The *Lubbar-fiend* seems to be the same traditionary being that is mentioned by Beaumont and Fletcher. " There is a pretty tale of a witch " that had the devil's mark about her, (god bless us !) that had a gy- " aunt to her son, that was called *Lob-lye-by-the-fire.*" *Knight of the*
Burning

Hughes, not considering our author's common practice of misspelling a word for the convenience of his rhyme, makes him guilty of many dissonant rhymes: for that editor, among other examples of his exactness, has reduced Spenser's text to modern orthography with great accuracy.

Burning Pestle, act. 3. sc. 1. These old stories were not entirely forgotten in Milton's younger days.

The two last lines are plainly founded on those in the old song of *Robin Goodfellow*, printed by Peck.

    When larks gin sing,
    Away we fling.

The following lines in the *Paradise Regained*, are illustrated by Peck.

  - - - - - Eeasts of chase, or fowl of game
  In pastry built, or from the spit, or boil'd,
  Gris-amber-steam'd. - - - - - -   b. 2. v. 342.

He observes, that in the reigns of Henry viii. and queen Elizabeth, ambergrease was applied as a seasoning in cookery; particularly at a stately banquet made by cardinal Wolsey. But, I must add, the practice was continued much later, and probably was not obsolete in the age of Milton. Thus Drayton, in the *Moone-Calfe*, printed in 1627.

  Eates capons cookt at fifteene crownes apiece,
  With their fat bellies stufft with *amber-greece*.

Where Ambergrease appears to have been a very costly ingredient; and indeed as such it is mentioned by Milton, who is representing a feast celebrated with all possible splendor and luxury. Ambergrease is mentioned much after the same manner, in Brown's *Britannia's Pastorals*. 1613.

  - - - - - - - - Her husband, weaken'd piece,
  Must have his cullis mix'd with *amber grease*:
  Pheasant and partridge into jelly turn'd,
  Grated with gold. - - - - - - - - b. 2. s. 3. p. 58.

It is indeed surprising upon the whole, that Spenser should execute a poem of uncommon length, with so much spirit and ease, laden as he was with so many shackles, and embarrassed with so complicated a BONDAGE of RIMING. Nor can I recollect, that he has been so careless as to suffer the same word to be repeated as a rhyme to itself, in more than four or five instances; a fault, which if he had more frequently committed, his manifold beauties of versification would have obliged us to overlook; and which Harrington should have avoided more scrupulously, to compensate, in some degree, for the tameness and prosaic mediocrity of his numbers.

Notwithstanding our author's frequent and affected usage of obsolete words and phrases*, yet it may

---

* The author of the *Arte of English Poesie* seems to blame Spenser for this. " Our *Maker* therefore, at these dayes, shall not follow Piers " Plowman, nor Gower, nor Lydgate, nor yet Chaucer; for their " language is now out of use with us." b. 3. c. 1.
The *Fairy Queen* was not published when this critic wrote, so that this censure is levelled at the *Pastorals*, which, however, in another place he commends, " For eglogue and pastoral poesie, Sir Philip " Sydney, and Maister Challener, and *that other gentleman* who wrote " the late *Shepherd's Kalender*." b. 1. c. 31. Spenser had published his *Pastorals* about ten years before; to which he did not prefix his name.
One of Spenser's cotemporary poets has ridiculed the obsolete language of the *Fairy Queen*.
   Let others sing of Knights and Palladines,
    In *aged* accents, and *untimely* words.
          DANIEL. *sonnet* lii.

be

be affirmed, that his ſtyle, in general, has great perſpicuity and facility. It is alſo remarkable, that his lines are ſeldom broken by tranſpoſitions, antitheſes, or parentheſes. His ſenſe and ſound are equally flowing and uninterrupted. From this ſingle conſideration, an internal argument ariſes, which plainly demonſtrates that *Britaine's Ida* is not written by Spenſer. Let the reader judge from the following ſpecimen.

> Amongſt the reſt, that all the reſt excell'd,
> A daintie boy there wonn'd, whoſe harmleſſe yeares
> Now in their freſheſt budding gentlie ſwell'd:
> His nymph-like face ne'er felt the nimble ſheeres,
> Youth's downie bloſſome through his cheek appeares;
> His lovelie limbes (but love he quite diſcarded),
> Were made for play, (but he no play regarded);
> And fitt love to reward, and be with love rewarded.

> High was his forehead, arch'd with ſilver mould,
> (Where never anger churliſh wrinkle dighted),
> His auburn lockes hung like dark threads of gold,
> That wanton airs (with their faire length incited)
> To play among their wanton curles delighted.
> His ſmiling eyes with ſimple truth were ſtord;
> Ah! how ſhould truth in thoſe thief eyes be ſtord;
> Which thouſand loves had ſtoln, and never once reſtord.

His chearfull lookes, and merie face would prove
(If eyes the index be where thoughts are read)
A daintie play-fellow for naked love.
Of all the other parts, &c*. — — —

But there are other arguments which prove this poem to be the work of a different hand. It has a vein of pleafing defcription; but is, at the fame time, filled with conceits and witticifms, of which Spenfer has much fewer, than might be expected from the tafte of his age. It's manner is like that of Fletcher's *Purple Ifland*. I fufpect it to have been written in imitation of Shakefpeare's *Venus and Adonis*‡. The author, whoever he was, certainly lived about the latter end of Elizabeth, or the beginning of James I.

Our author's *Paftorals* are written in profeffed imitation of Chaucer's ftyle. This he tells us exprefsly in the beginning of *Colin Clouts come home again*.

The fhepherd's boy, beft knowen by that name,
That after TITYRUS † firft fung his lay.

---

* Spenfer's works, Lond. 1750. vol. 6. pag. 34. duod.

‡ The firft Edition of which was printed, London, for William Leake, 1602, 12mo.

† Milton, in imitation of our author, ftyles Chaucer TITYRUS, where he hints at Chaucer's having travelled into Italy.

Quin et in has quondam pervenit TITYRUS oras.

Manfus, v. 34.

And

And the tale of the *Oak* and *Brier*, in the Eclogue of *Februarie*, is more peculiarly modelled after Chaucer's manner, and is accordingly thus introduced.

— — — — A tale of truth
Which I cond of Tityrus in my youth.

And in another paſtoral he hints at his having copied Chaucer.

That *Colin* hight which well could pipe and ſing,
For he of Tityrus his ſong did lere.

In the *Paſtorals* he likewiſe appears to have attempted an imitation of the *Viſions* of *Pierce Plowman*; for after exhorting his muſe not to contend with Chaucer, he adds,

Nor with the Plowman that the pilgrim playde awhile *.

And beſides, that his *Paſtorals* might, in every reſpect, have the air of a work in old engliſh, he has adopted and given them the title of an old book, called the Shepheard's Kalender †, firſt printed by Wynkin de Worde, and reprinted about twenty years before he publiſhed theſe Paſtorals, viz. 1559. This

* Epilogue to *Shep. Kalend.*

† Hearne calls this piece, " *a comical odd book*, of which I have an " imperfect copy, and look upon it as a great Curiosity." Not. ad Gul. Neubrig. vol. 3. pag. 749.

is what E. K. means, where he fays in his epiftle prefixed, " He tearmeth it the SHEPHERD's KALENDER, " applying an *old name* to a *new* work." One of Spenfer's reafons for ufing fo much antient phrafeology in thefe Paftorals, was undoubtedly the obvious one of cloathing rural characters in the drefs of doric fimplicity; but the principal reafon is moft probably, that which is delivered by his friend and commentator, E. K *. who was " privie to all his defigns:"—
" In myne opinion, it is one efpecial prayfe of many
" which are due to this poet, that he hath laboured
" to reftore, as to their rightful heritage, fuch good
" and natural englifh words, as have been long time
" out of ufe, and almoft cleane difherited; which is
" the only caufe that our mother-tongue, which truly
" of itfelfe is both *full enough for profe*, and *ftately enough*
" *for verfe*, hath long time beene counted moft bare
" and barren of both; which default, when as fome
" have endeavoured to falve and recure, they patched
" up the holes with peeces and ragges of other lan-
" guages; borrowing here of the french, there of the
" italian, and every where of the latine; not weigh-
" ing how ill thofe tongues accord with themfelves,

* Some have thought that his Name was Kerke. I fuppofe, becaufe Spenfer, in his letters to Harvey, mentions his lodging with one Mrs. Kerke, and, in the fame, fends E. K's compliments to Harvey.

but

" but much worfe with ours; fo now they have made
" our englifhe tongue a gallimaufrey, or hodge-podge
" of all other fpeeches *." Thus that which induced
Spenfer to adopt fo much obfolete language in the Paftorals, induced him likewife to do the fame in the
FAIRY QUEEN. Hence too it appears, that he was
difgufted with the practice of his cotemporary writers,
who had adulterated, according to his judgment, the
purity of the englifh tongue by various innovations
from the fpanifh, french, latin, and italian. And
that this was a prevailing affectation in the age of
queen Elizabeth, may be concluded from the following paffages.

Thus Marfton in his *Satires.*

> I cannot quote a *motte italianate;*
> Or brand my Satires with a *fpanifh terme* †.

Bifhop Hall in his *Satires,* publifhed in 1597.

> There if he can with termes *italianate,*
> Big-founding fentences, &c. — —

And Camden having given us a fpecimen of the
Lord's prayer in old englifh has thefe words. " Hi-
" therto will our fparkfull youth laugh at their great

---

* Ibid. † Proem. b. 2.

" grand-

"grand-fathers englifh, who had more care tò do well, than to fpeak minion-like; and left more glory to us by their exploiting great actes, than we fhall by our forging new words, and uncouth phrafes*." A learned gentleman, one R. C. [Carew] who has addreffed a letter to Camden, inferted in that author's REMAINS, thus fpeaks. "So have our italian travellers brought us acquainted of their fweet-relifhed phrafes; even we feeke to make our good of our late fpanifh enemie, and fear as little the hurt of his tongue, as the dint of his fword." Again, "We within thefe fixty years have incorporated fo many latin and french words, as the third part of our tongue confifteth now in them." And Afcham in his *Schole-mafter* informs us, that not only the language, but the manners, of Italy had totally infected his country-men, where he is defcribing the ITALIANIZED ENGLISHMAN†.

* REMAINS. Artic. LANGUAGES.

† The fame author acquaints us, that about this time an infinite number of italian books were tranflated into englifh: among the reft, were many italian novels, the tranflations of which, Shakefpeare manifeftly made ufe ot for fome of his plots. Thofe who have undertaken to point out the books from whence Shakefpeare borrowed his plots, have not, I think, been able to difcover the fource from whence he drew the ftory of his MERCHANT of VENICE; which, in all probability, is founded upon the following antient ballad, which I met with in a large collection. *Muf. Afhmol.* Oxon. Cod. impreff. A. Wood.

A SONG

Our author's disapprobation of this practice appears more fully from his own words, where he expresly

A SONG, *shewing the crueltie of* Gernutus *a* JEWE, *who lending to a marchant an hundred crownes, would have a pound of his fleshe, because he could not pay him at the time appointed.*

> In Venice towne not long agoe,
>   A cruell JEWE did dwell;
> Which lived all on usurie,
>   As italian writers tell.
>
> GERNUTUS called was the Jewe, &c.

The whole song would be too prolix for this place. I shall transcribe only the close of the story; having premised, that the cunning and rapacious Jew is represented, in our ballad, to have lent an eminent merchant of Venice an hundred crowns, upon a bond, in which promise of payment is made within a year and a day; under the forfeiture of a pound of the merchant's flesh, in case of non-payment: that the merchant, on account of his ships being detained by contrary winds, was unable to perform his contract at the time appointed: that the affair was referred to a judge; that the friends of the merchant offered ten thousand crowns to absolve him, but that the Jew obstinately persisted in his demand of the forfeited pound of flesh.

> Then said the judge, Yet good, my friend,
>   Let me of you desire,
>
> To take the flesh from such a place
>   As yet you let him live;
> Doe so, and loe an hundred crownes
>   To thee here I will give.
>
> No, no, quoth he, &c.
> * * * * * *
> For I will have my pound of fleshe,
>   From under his right side.
> * * * * * *

hints that Chaucer's language, which he so closely copied, was the pure English.

>The bloudie Jewe now readie is,
> With whetted blade in hand,
>To spoyle the bloude of innocent,
> By forfeit of his bond.
>
>And as he was about to strike
> In him the deadlie blow,
>Stay (quoth the judge) thy crueltie,
> I charge thee to do so.
>
>Sith needs thou wilt thy forfeit have
> Which is of fleshe a pound;
>See that thou shed no drop of bloud,
> Nor yet the man confound.
>
>For if thou doe, like murderer
> Thou here shall hanged bee,
>Likewise of fleshe see that thou cut
> No more than longs to thee;
>
>For if thou take or more or lesse
> To value of a mite,
>Thou shalt be hanged presentlie,
> As is both law and right.
>
>Gernutus nowe waxt franticke mad,
> And wote not what to say;
>Quoth he at last, ten thousand crownes
> I will that he shall pay;
>
>And so I grant to sette him free,
> The judge doth answer make,
>You shall not have a peny given,
> Your forfeiture now take.
>
>At the last he doth demand
> But for to have his owne;
>No, (quoth the judge) doe as you list,
> Thy judgment shall be showne;

— Dan Chaucer WELL of ENGLISH UNDEFILDE *.

4. 2. 32.

> Either take your pound of fleshe, qd he,
>   Or cancell me your bond;
> O cruel judge! then quoth the Jewe,
>   That doth against me stand.
>
> And so with griped grieved mind,
>   He biddeth them farewell,
> All the people prais'd the Lord,
>   That ever this heard tell.

After which follows a moral exhortation, resulting from the subject. But the whole may be seen in the CONNOISSEUR, vol. i. No. 16.

It may be objected, that this ballad might have been written after, and copied from, Shakespeare's play. But if that had been the case, it is most likely that the author would have preserved Shakespeare's name of Shylock for the Jew; and nothing is more likely, than that Shakespeare in copying from this ballad, should alter the name from Gernutus to one more Jewish; and by the alteration of the name his imitation was the better disguised. Another argument, which would have appeared much more convincing, had the whole song been transcribed, but which perhaps will be allowed from this extract, is, that our ballad has the air of a narrative written before Shakespeare's play; I mean that if it had been written after the play, it would have been much more full and circumstantial: At present, it has too much the nakedness of an original. Besides, the first stanza informs us, that the story was taken from some italian novel. Thus much therefore is certain, that is, Shakespeare either copied from that italian novel, or from this ballad: Now we have

no

---

* A learned and sagacious lexicographer gives a very different account of the purity of Chaucer's style. " *Chaucerus, pessimo exemplo, integris vocum plaustris ex eadem Gallia in nostram linguam invectis; eam, nimis antea a Normannorum victoria adulteratam, omni fere nativa gratia et nitore spoliavit, pro genuinis coloribus fucum illinens, pro vera facie larvam inducens.*" Skinner, *Præfat. ad Etymolog. Ling. Anglic.*

But although Spenſer diſapproved of this corrupt adulteration of ſtyle, ſo faſhionable in his age, yet we find him notwithſtanding, frequently introducing words from a foreign tongue, ſuch as, *viſnomie, amenance, arret, meſpriſe, ſovenance, afrap, aguiſe, amenage, obaſe*, and the like; but theſe words the frequent return of his rhyme obliged him to introduce, and accordingly they will generally be found at the end of his lines. The poverty of our tongue, or rather the unfrequency of it's identical terminations, compelled him likewiſe, for the ſake of rhyme, perpetually to coin new engliſh words, ſuch as *damnify'd, unmercify'd, wonderment, warriment, unruliment, habitaunce, hazardrie*, &c. &c. To this cauſe his many latiniſms alſo may be attributed, which, like all the reſt, are ſubſtituted to make out the neceſſary jingle.

no tranſlation, I preſume, of ſuch a novel into engliſh; if then it be granted, that Shakeſpeare generally took his italian ſtories from their engliſh tranſlations, and that the arguments above, concerning the prior antiquity of this ballad are true, it will follow that Shakeſpeare copied from this ballad.

I ſhall only add, that it appears from S. Goſſon's *Schoole of Abuſe*, printed in 1579; that the character *of a cruel and covetous Jew* had been exhibited with good applauſe, before Shakeſpeare's *Shylock* appeared. The author is commending ſome plays, and among the reſt, " The JEWE " and Ptolome ſhewne at the *bull*; the one repreſenting *the greedineſſe of " worldly chuſers, and bloudy minds of Uſurers*, the other, &c."

The

The censure of Jonson, upon our author's style, is perhaps unreasonable: " Spenser, in affecting the an-" tients, writ no language*." The ground-work and substance of his style is the language of his age. This indeed is seasoned with various expressions, adopted from the elder poets; but in such a manner, that the language of his age was rather strengthened and dignified, than debased or disguised, by such a practice. In truth, the affectation of Spenser in this point, is by no means so striking and visible, as Jonson has insinuated; nor is his phraseology so difficult and obsolete, as it is generally supposed to be. For many stanzas together, we may frequently read him with as much facility, as we can the same number of lines in Shakespeare.

But although I cannot subscribe to Jonson's opinion concerning Spenser's language, I must confess that the following sentiments of that critic, concerning the use of old words in poetry, are admirable. " Words " borrowed of antiquity do lend a kind of majesty to " style, and are not without their delight sometimes. " For they have the authority of yeares, and out of " their intermission do lend a kind of grace-like new-" nesse. BUT THE ELDEST OF THE PRESENT,

* DISCOVERIES.

" AND

" AND THE NEWEST OF THE PAST LANGUAGE
" IS THE BEST *." But Jonson has literally tranf-
lated the latter part of the paragraph, from Quintilian,
without acknowledgment. " ERGO UT NOVORUM
" OPTIMA ERUNT MAXIME VETERA, ITA VETE-
" RUM MAXIME NOVA †."

I conclude this Section with a passage from the ner-
vous, poetical, and witty Satires of bishop Hall; who
having censured the petty poets of his age, for their various corruptions, and licentious abuses, of the english
language, makes this compliment to Spenser.

> But lett no rebel satyr dare traduce
> Th' eternall Legends of thy FAERIE MUSE,
> Renowned SPENSER! whom no earthly wight
> Dares once to emulate, much less despight.
> *Salust* of France, and Tuscan *Ariost*!
> Yield up the lawrel-girlond ye have lost:
> And lett all others willows wear with mee,
> Or lett their undeserving temples bared bee ‡.

* DISCOVERIES.   † Inftit. Or. l. 1. cap. 6.

‡ B. 1. f. 4. These satires [the three first books] were first printed by T. Creede, for R. Dexter, Lond. 1597. 12mo. The three last books appeared in an edition entitled, " *Virgidemiarum*, The three last bookes of
" *byting* Satyres, *Anon.* Lond. printed by R. Bradocke, for R. Dexter,
" &c. 1598." 12mo. It begins with sat. 1. of lib. 4. The next edition
[of the whole] is, " *Virgidemiarum*, The three last [in reality all the
" six] bookes of the *byting* Satyres, corrected and amended, with some

SECT. V.

Of Spenser's Imitations from Chaucer.

IT has been before observed in general, that Spenser copied the language of Chaucer: and it is evident, that in many passages he has imitated Chaucer's sentiment. It is frequently true, that parallelists mistake *Resemblances* for *Thefts*. But this doctrine by no means affects the instances which I shall give in this section, of Spenser's imitations from Chaucer, and which I shall produce in the next, of the passages he has copied from Ariosto. Spenser is universally acknowledged to have been an attentive reader, and a professed admirer, of both these poets. His imitations from the former are most commonly literal, couched in the expressions of the original. What he has drawn from Ariosto are artificial fictions, which

---

" additions, by J. H. Lond. for R. Dexter, &c. 1599." 12mo. In a copy I have seen of this last edition, at the end are bound up, " Certaine " worthye manuscript poems of great antiquitie, reserved long in the " studie of a Northfolke Gentleman, now first published by J. S. Lond. " R. D. 1597." 12mo. The poems are, " The stately Tragedy of " Guiscard and Sismond." In two books, in the seven-lined stanza. It is Dryden's story, and seems about the age of Henry vii. " The " Northern Mother's Blessing, written nine yeares before the death of " G. Chaucer." " The Way to Thrift." They are dedicated to the worthiest poet MAISTER ED. SPENSER,

consisting

consisting of unnatural combinations, could not, on account of their singularity, be fallen upon by both poets accidentally, as natural appearances might be, which lie exposed and obvious to all, at all times. We may therefore safely pronounce the resemblances in the sections here mentioned, to have been intended.

But I proceed to collect some specimens of Spenser's imitations from Chaucer, both of language and sentiment.

B. i. c. i. s. viii.

> Much can they praise the trees so straight and high,
> The sayling pine, the cedar proud and tall,
> The vine-prop elme, the poplar never dry,
> The builder oake, sole king of forests all,
> The aspine good for staves, the cypresse funeral.

ix.

> The laurell, meed of mighty conquerours,
> And poets sage; the firre that weepeth still,
> The willow, worne of forlorne paramours,
> The eugh, obedient to the bender's will,
> The birch for shafts, the fallow for the mill,
> The myrrhe sweet-bleeding in the bitter wound.
> The warlike beech, the ash for nothing ill,
> The fruitfull olive, and the platane round,
> The carver holme, the maple sildom inward found.

Ovid,

(137)

Ovid [*], Seneca [†], Lucan [‡], Statius [§], and Claudian [||], have all left us a defcription of trees; but Spenfer, in this before us, feems more immediately to have had his favorite Chaucer in his eye; he has, however, much improved upon the brevity and fimplicity of our antient bard.

> The builder oake, and eke the hardie afhe,
> The pillar elme, the coffir unto caraine,
> The boxe pipe-tree, holme to whips lafhe,
> The failing firre, the cipres death to plaine,
> The fhooter ewe, the afpe for fhaftes plaine,
> The olive of peace, and eke the dronken vine,
> The victor palme, the laurer to divine [*].

In Chaucer's *Complaint of the Blacke Knight*, we meet with another defcription of trees, from which Spenfer feems to have collected and added one or two circumftances.

> The mirre alfo that weepeth ever' of kinde :
> The cedris hie, as upright as a line [†].

Spenfer, perhaps, in this minute and particular enumeration of various trees, has incurred lefs cenfure

---

[*] Met. 10. 90.   [†] Oedip. 532.   [‡] 3. 440.   [§] Theb. 6. 98.
[||] R. Proferp. 2. 107.   The paffages are alledged by Dr. Jortin, *Remarks on Spenfer's Poems*, p. 4, 5.   [*] The Affemble of Fowles, v. 176.   [†] Ver. 66.

T

than

than some of the roman authors mentioned above. In some of those indeed, such a description will be found superfluous and impertinent; but, upon this occasion, it is highly consistent, and even expedient, that the poet should dwell, for some time, on the beauty of this grove, in describing it's variety of trees, as that circumstance tends to draw the red-crofs knight and his companions farther and farther into the shade, 'till at length they are imperceptibly invited to the cave of error, which stood in the thickest part of it. This description is so far from being puerile, or ill-placed, that it serves to improve and illustrate the allegory. But notwithstanding this may be affirmed in vindication of Spenser, I am apt to think, that the impropriety of introducing such a description, would not have appeared a sufficient reason to our poet for not admitting it.

The reader will excuse my producing another passage from Chaucer, in which he ridicules, with no less humour than judgment, the particular detail of trees, and of the circumstances that followed upon their being felled, given us by one of the above-mentioned antient poets. He is speaking of Arcite's funeral.

> But how the fire was maken up on height,
> And eke the names, how all the trees hight,

As oke, firre beech, afpe, elder, elme, popelere,
Willow, holme, plane, boxe, cheften, and laurere,
Maple, thorne, beech, ewe, hafell, whipultree,
How they were feld, fhall not be told for me,
Ne how the gods runnen up and,
Difherited of her habitatioun,
In which they wonned in reft and pees,
Nymphes, Faunies, Amadriades.
Ne how the beafts ne how the birds all
Fledden for feare, when the trees was fall ‡.

But a ridicule of this kind was ftill more proper, as the popular poems of his times, often abounded with inftances of prolix and needlefs numerations. Thus in the *Squyre of Lowe Degree* *, an old piece, perhaps coeval with Chaucer.

— — In the arbor was a tree
A fayrer in the world might none bee;
The tree was of cyprefle
The firft tre that Jefu chafe *,

‡ Knight's tale, v. 2992.
* London, imprinted for W. Copland, 4to.
* Alluding to the tradition that the crofs was made of this wood.
* *Signature* a, ii b.

From this paffage, and another of the fame fort in the fame piece, an ingenious correfpondent has taken occafion to confider Chaucer's *Rime of Sir Thopas* in a new light. I will tranfcribe his words. " The Rhyme of Sir Thopas was intended by Chaucer, as a kind of burlefque on the old ballad romances; many of which he quotes,

T 2   Men

The fother wood, and fycamoure,
The reed rofe, and the lyly floure,
The box, the beache, and the larel tree:
The date, alfo the damysé,
The fylbyrdes hanging to the ground,
The fyg tree, and the maple round;
And other tres ther was mane ane;
The piany, the popler, and the plane.
The broad branches all aboute,
Within the arbour and withoute †.

Afterwards follows a catalogue of birds in the fame manner. But Chaucer is often guilty of the fault he here condemns.

   Men fpeken of Romaunces of prife,
   Of Hornechild, and Ipotis,
    Of Bevis, and Sir Gie,
   Of Sir Libeaux, &c.

Moſt of theſe, at leaſt fuch of them as I have feen, are in the very fame metre with *Sir Thopas*, and were fung to the harp, as appears from your own quotation. (pag. 49. fupr.) Now in thefe old romances nothing is fo common, as impertinent digreffions, containing affected enumerations of trees, birds, &c. There is a fpecimen of the former in an old romance intitled, *the Squyer of lowe degre:* where it is remarkable, that the author has reckoned the *lily*, the *piany*, the *fother-wood*, &c. as trees. With the fame accuracy the *pie*, the *papinjay*, the *fparrow*, &c. are claffed among the finging birds, in the lines which immediately follow the lift of trees, viz.

   On every braunche fat byrdes thre,
   Singing with great melody,
   The laverocke and the nightingale,
   The ruddocke, the woodwale,

B. i. c. xii. f. xiv.

The poet is speaking of the magnificent feasting, after the red-crosse knight had conquered the dragon.

> What needs me tell their feast, and goodly guise,
> In which was nothing riotous, nor vaine?
> What needs of dainty dishes to devise,
> Of comely services, or courtly traine?
> My narrow leaves cannot in them containe,
> The large discourse of royal princes state.

> The *pee*, and the *popinjaye*,
> The thrustle sunge bothe night and daye,
> The *martyn* and the wrenne also,
> The *swallowe* whippinge too and fro,
> The jaye jangled them amonge,
> The larke began that mery songe,
> The *sparrowe* spredde her on her spraye
> The mavis sange with her notes full gaye,
> The *nuthake* with her notes newe,
> The *sterlynge*, &c.
> - - - - - Sunge with notes clere,
> In confortinge that Squyere.

From these lines we shall easily perceive the drift of Chaucer's humour in the following stanzas of *Sir Thopas*.

> There springen herbes grete and smal,
> The lycores and the setuall,
> And many a clove gelofer,
> And *nutmeges* to put in *ale*,
> Whether it be newe or stale,
> Or for to lie in cofer.

The

(142)

To this I shall beg leave to subjoin another passage of the same kind; in which he is describing the wedding of Florimel.

> To tell the glory of the feast that day,
> The goodly service, the devisefull sights,
> The bridegroomes state, the brides most rich array,
> The pride of ladies, and the worth of knights,
> The royall banquetts, and the rare delights,
> Were worke fit for an herauld*, not for me.
>
> 5. 3. 3

> The birdes singen, it is no naie,
> The *sperhawke*, and the *popinjaye*,
>   That joye it was to here;
> The throstell eke made his laye,
> The *wood-cocke* upon the spraye,
>   She song full loud and clere.

These lines are transcribed from an old black letter edition of Chaucer, which wants the title: but in Speght's and Urry's editions, they are somewhat different; the latter having substituted *wood-larke* instead of *wood-cock*, not considering that Chaucer is jocose."

* Many of the historical romances, of the middle age, were written by heralds. Vid. Le Pere Menestrier, *Chevalerie ancienne*, &c. Paris, 12mo. 1683, ch. 5. pag. 225. In Worcester-college library, at Oxford, there is a beautiful manuscript on vellom, written in short french verse, describing the atchievements of Edward the Black Prince. It was composed by the prince's herald, who attended him close by his person, in all his wars, as was the custom. This was the Chandois-herald, and he is frequently mentionéd in Froissart. The Copy is very fairly written, the names of the englishmen rightly spelled, the chronology exact, and the epitaph of the Black Prince, which closes the poem, is the same as the prince ordered in his will. It is an oblong octavo, and formerly belonged to Sir William Le Neve, Clarencieux-herald. I have transcribed the prose argument to the first part. " *Cy commence une partie de*
la

After this indirect, but comprehensive manner, Chaucer expresses the pomp of Cambuscan's feast.

> Of which shall I tell all the array,
> Then would it occupie a sommer's day;
> And eke it needeth not to devise
> At every course the order of service.
> I wol not tellen as now, of her strange sewes,
> Ne of her swans, ne of her heronsewes.
> Eke in that land, as tellen knights old,
> There is some meat that is fully dainty hold,
> That in this lond men retch of it but small:
> There is no man that may reporten all *.

Thus also, when lady Cuftance is married to the Sowdan of Surrie, or Syria.

> What shuld I tellen of the rialte
> Of that wedding? or which course goth beforn?
> Who blowith in a trompe, or in a horne †?

In these passages it is very evident, that Chaucer intended a burlesque upon the tedious and elaborate descriptions of such unimportant circumstances, so frequent in books of chivalry. In the last verse the burlesque is very strong.

---

la vie et des faites d'armes d'une tresnoble Prince de Gaules et d'Aquitaine qu'avoit au noun Edward, l'eigne filitz au roy Edward tierce queux dieux assoile."

* Squire's tale, v. 83.   † The man of lawe's tale. v. 704.

It should seem that in some of the old romances, the names of trumpeters in the lists were sometimes mentioned. Chaucer places in the *House of Fame*,

> — — All that usid clarion
> In Casteloigne and Arragon,
> That in their timis famous were *.

B. i. c. xii. s. xxiv.

He is speaking of a grand assembly, which is held in the hall of the palace of Una's father.

> With flying speed, and seeming great pretence,
> Came running in, much like a man dismaid,
> A messenger with letters, which his message said.

XXV.

> All in the open hall amazed stood,
> At suddennesse of that unwarie sight,
> And wondred at his breathlesse hastie mood;
> But he for nought would stay his passage right,
> Till fast before the king he did alight,
> Where falling flat great humblesse he did make,
> And kist the ground whereon his foot was pight.

He seems to have copied this surprise, occasioned in the hall by the sudden and unexpected entrance

* 3. 157.

of a meſſenger, together with ſome of the concomitant circumſtances, from a ſimilar but more alarming ſurpriſe in Chaucer, which happened at Cambuſcan's annual birth-day feſtival.

> And ſo befell, that aftir the third courſe,
> While that the king ſat thus in his noblay,
> Herk'ning his minſtrelis their thingis play,
> Beforn him at his bord deliciouſly;
> In at the halle dore full ſodeinly
> There came a knight upon a ſtede of braſs;
> And in his hond, &c. &c.
> * * * * * * * * *
> And up he rideth to the hie bord;
> In all the hall ne was there ſpoke a word;
> For marveile of this knight, him to behold
> Full beſily they waiten yong, and old.
> This ſtraunge knight, &c.
> * * * * * * * * *
> Salved the king and quene, and lordis all,
> By ordir, as they ſittin in the hall,
> With ſo hie reverence and obeiſaunce,
> As well in ſpeche, as in countinaunce,
> That, &c. &c.
> * * * * * * * *
> And aftir this, beforn the hie bord,
> He with a manly voice ſaide his meſſage *.

* Squier's tale, v. 96.

These sudden entrances of strange and unexpected personages, when feasts were magnificently celebrated in great halls, in the ages of chivalry, seem to have been no uncommon incident; either for diversion of the guests, or exhibiting complaints, or encrease of the solemnity. Stowe has recorded an instance of this sort.

"In the yeare 1316, Edward II. did solemnize his
"feast of Pentecost, at Westminster, in the great
"hall, where sitting royally at the table, with his
"peares about him, there entred a woman adorned
"like a minstrell, sitting on a great horse trapped as
"minstrelles then used, who rode round about the ta-
"bles, shewing pastime, and at length came up to
"the king's table, and laide before him a letter, and
"forthwith turning her horse, saluted every one, and
"departed. The letters being opened, had these
"contents: Our soveraigne lord the king hath no-
"thing courteously respected his knights, that in his
"father's time, &c*. The ceremony of our champion at the coronation, the only genuine remainder of chivalry subsisting in modern times, is much in the spirit of this custom.

* Stowe's Survey of London, pag. 387. ed. 1599.

B. ii. c. xii. f. li.

Thereto the heavens alwaies joviall
Lookt on them lovely, ſtill in ſtedfaſt ſtate,
Ne ſuffer'd ſtorme, nor froſt on them to fall,
Their tender buds or leaves to violate,
Nor ſcorching heat, nor cold intemperate,
T 'afflict the creatures which therein did dwell;
But the milde aire with ſeaſon moderate,
Gently attempred and diſpos'd ſo well,
That ſtill it breathed forth ſweet ſpirit and holeſome ſmell.

Chaucer in the *Aſſemble of Fowles*.

The air of the place ſo attempre was,
That nether was ther grevance of hot ne cold,
There was eke every holeſome ſpice and gras,
Ne no man may there waxe ſicke ne olde [*].

As a proof of the imitation, it may be obſerved, that Spenſer has not only here borrowed ſome of Chaucer's thoughts, but ſome of his words. He might nevertheleſs, have ſome paſſages in the †claſſics in his eye, cited by Dr. Jortin ‡; particularly, a beautiful deſcription in Lucretius.

[*] Ver. 204.

† Claudian. N. Hon. et Mar. v. 51. Lucret. 3. v. 18. Hom. Odyſſ. 6. v. 42. Sidon. Car. 2. v. 407.

‡ Remarks, p. 74. 75.

B. iii. c. ii. f. xix.

The poet, among other rare qualities of Merlin's wonderous mirrour, mentions the following,

> Whatever foe had wrought, or friend had fayn'd
> Therein difcovered was. — —

And afterwards ft. 21.

> Such was the glaffie globe that Merlin made,
> And gave unto king * Ryence for his guard,
> That never foes his kingdom might invade,
> But he it knew at home, before he hard
> Tidings thereof, and fo them ftill debard.
> It was a famous prefent for a prince,
> And worthy worke of infinite reward,
> That treafons could betray, and foes convince.

It is manifeft that Spenfer drew the idea of this mirrour, from that which is prefented by the ftrange knight to Cambufcan, in Chaucer.

> This mirrour eke, which I have in my hond,
> Hath foche a might, that men may in it fe
> Whan there fhall fall any adverfite
> Unto your reigne, or to yourfelf alfo,
> And opin fe who is your frend or fo.

* A king often mentioned in MORTE ARTHUR.

And over all, if any lady bright
Hath fet her hert on any manir wight,
If he be falfe fhe fhall the trefoun fe,
His newe love, and all his fubtilte,
So opinly, that there fhall nothing hide [*].

Spenfer likewife feigns, that his mirror was of fervice in the purpofes of love; and as fuch it is confulted by Britomartis, but upon an occafion different from that which is here mentioned by Chaucer. She looks in it with a defign to difcover her deftined hufband.

Whom fortune for her hufband would allott.
ft. 23.

As the ufes of this mirror were of fo important a nature, Spenfer ought not to have firft mentioned it to us by that light appellation, *Venus' Looking Glafs*; where he is fpeaking of Britomart's love for Arthegall,

Whofe image fhe had feen in Venus' looking glafs.
3. 1. 8.

B. iii. c. ix. f. xxviii.

She fent at him one firie dart, whofe hed
Empoyfned was with privie luft, and jelous dred.

[*] Squier's tale, v. 153.

xxix.

Hee from that deadly throwe made no defence,
But to the wound his weake heart opened wide,
The wicked engine thro' falfe influence
Paft through his eyes, and fecretly did glyde,
Into his hart, which it did forely gryde.

Which feem to refemble thefe of Chaucer. He is fpeaking of Cupid.

He took an arrow full fharpely whet,
And in his bowe when it was fett,
He ftreight up to his eare drough
The ftrong bowe that was fo tough,
And fhot at me fo wonder fmert,
That through mine eye unto mine hert
The takell fmote, and deep it went [*].

The thought of the heart being wounded through the eye occurs again in Chaucer.

So that this arrow anone right
Throughout eye, as it was found,
Into mine hert hath made a wound [†].

Thus alfo Palamon fpeaks, after he had feen Emely.

But I was hurt right now through mine eie
Into mine hert [‡]. — — —

---

[*] Rom. of Rofe. v. 1723.   [†] Ibid. 1778.   [‡] Knights tale, v. 1098.

The thought likewise occurs again, in our poet's second *Hymne in honour of Beautie.*

> Hath white and red in it such wondrous powre
> That it can pierce through th' eyes unto the hart?

And in the first Hymn on the same subject. Butler has founded a pleasant image on this thought.

> Love is a burglarer, a felon,
> That at the windore-eye doth steale in
> To rob the heart, and with his prey
> Steals out again another way*.

> B. iv. c. ii. s. xxxii.

Whylome, as antique stories tellen us,
Those two, &c.
* * * * * * * *
Though now their acts be no where to be found,
As that renowned poet them compiled,
With warlike numbers, and heroick sound,
Dan Chaucer, well of English undefiled,
On fame's eternal bead-roll worthy to be filed.

The *Squier's Tale* of Chaucer being imperfect †, our poet thus introduces his story of the battle of the

---

* Hudib. par. 2. cant. 1. 417.

† Not unfinished, for a very good reason offered by the judicious Mr. Upton, who says, "I hardly think that a story promising so fair in the beginning, should be left HALF-TOLD." Letter to G. West, Esq; p. 10.

three brethren for Canace; which he builds upon the following hint of Chaucer.

> And after woll I speke of Camballo,
> That fought in listis with the brethren two,
> For Canace, er that they might her winn.

But with these lines the story breaks off.

Mr. Upton * calls this addition of Spenser to Chaucer's fragment, a completion of the *Squier's Tale*; but it is certainly nothing more than a completion of one part or division of Chaucer's poem. For, besides what Chaucer proposed to speak of in the verses above-quoted concerning the contest for Canace, he intended likewise to tell us,

> How that his Falcon got her love againe,
> Repentant, as the story telleth us,
> By mediation of Camballus †.

Also,

> First woll I tell you of king Cambuscan
> That in his time many a cite wan,
> How that he wan Thedora to his wife;
> And after woll I speke of Algarsife,
> For whom full oft in grete peril he was,
> Ne had ben holpin, but by th' hors of bras ‡.

* Ubi supr. p. 10.   † Squier's tale. v. 674.   ‡ Ibid. v. 681.

(153)

It is no lefs amufing to the imagination, to bewilder itfelf in various conjectures, concerning the expedients by which thefe promifed events were brought about, and to indulge the difquifitions of fancy, about the many romantic miracles, that muft have been effected by this wonderful fteed, than it is difagreeable to reflect, that Chaucer's defcription of fuch matters is entirely loft. It appears that Milton was particularly fond of this poem; and that he was not a little defirous of knowing the remainder and end of a ftory which already difclofed fo many beauties. In *Il Penserofo* he invokes MELANCHOLY, to

 — Call up Him who left HALF-TOLD.
 The ftory of Cambufcan bold *.

But for what reafon are we to fuppofe that he defired this fabler to be CALLED-UP? Was it not for this purpofe, that Chaucer might finifh that part of the HALF-TOLD tale which yet remained *untold?* As he before requefts, that Orpheus might be fummoned to fing,

 Such notes as warbled to the ftring,
 Drew iron tears down Pluto's cheek †:

fo he does not here defire that Chaucer fhould be

* Ver. 109.   † Ibid. v. 105.

called

called up for nothing; but that the author of this imperfect tale of Cambuscan, should likewise tell,

> Of Camball and of Algarsife,
> And who had Canace to wife,
> That own'd the virtuous ring of glass,
> And of the wondrous horse of brass,
> On which the Tartar king did ride †.

Circumstances and incidents, which are not in the *half-told* story which Chaucer has left us, but which are only proposed to be told in Chaucer's verses above-cited, and were the subject of the lamented sequel.

Lydgate, in his TEMPLE OF GLAS, seems to speak as if he had seen a completed copy of this tale.

> And uppermore men depeinten might see,
> How, with her RING, goodly CANACE,
> Of everie fowle the leden and the song
> Could understand, as she hem walkt among:
> And how her brother so often holpen was
> In his mischefe, by the STEDE OF BRAS.

That part of the story which is hinted at in the two last lines, is lost; which however might have been remaining in the age of Lydgate.

In the Ashmolean Museum at Oxford, there is a

† Ibid. v. 111.

completion of this tale, by John Lane, in manuscript. The title of it is as follows, " CHAUCER's PILLER ; " beinge his master-piece, called the SQUIER's TALE; " which hath binn given for lost for almost theese " three hundred yeares, but now found out, and " brought to light, by JOHN LANE, 1630*." I conceived great expectations of this manuscript, on reading the following passage in Philips. " JOHN " LANE, a fine old Queen Elizabeth's gentleman, " who was living within my remembrance, and whose " several poems, had they not had the ill luck to " remain unpublished, when much better meriting " than many that are in print, might possibly have " gained him a name not inferior (if not equal) to " Drayton, and others of the next rank to SPENSER ; " but they are all to be produced in manuscript, " namely, his POETICAL VISION, his ALARM TO " POETS, his TWELVE MONTHS, his GUY OF " WARWICK, (an heroic poem, at least as much " as many others that are so entitled), and lastly, his " SUPPLEMENT to Chaucer's SQUIRE's TALE †." But I was greatly disappointed ; for Lane's performance, upon perusal, proved to be, not only an inarti-

---

* It is numbered in the catalogue, and in the first leaf, 6937. On the back, 53. quarto. Codd. Ashmol.
† *Theat*. *Poet*. Mod. Poets, pag. 112.

ficial imitation of Chaucer's manner, but a weak effort of invention. There is a more ancient manuscript copy of Lane's *Addition* to the SQUIRES TALE, in the library of New-College, at Oxford. It is, however, no rare manuscript.

I cannot omit this opportunity of expressing equal regret for the loss of great part of a noble old Scottish poem, entitled, HARDYKNUTE; which exhibits a striking representation of our antient martial manners, that prevailed, before alterations in government, and the conveniencies of civilised life, had introduced the general uniformities of fashion; and established that security, which necessarily excludes hazardous attempts and glorious dangers, so suitable to the character and genius of the heroic muse [*].

.B. iv. c. ii. f. xxxiii.

But wicked Time, that all good thoughts doth waste,
And workes of noblest wits to nought outweare,

---

[*] Since this was written, I have been assured upon good authority, that HARDYKNUTE is a modern piece. It was written by Mrs. ---- Halkett, aunt to Sir Peter Halkett, who was killed in America, with general Braddock, 1755. The late lord president Forbes was in the secret, and used to laugh at the deception of the world. It was written near fifty years ago, and never extended further than at present. But I am apt to think that the first stanza is old, and gave the hint for writing the rest.

That

That famous monument has quite defac'd;
* * * * * * * * *
O curſed Elde! the canker-worme of writs;
How may theſe rimes (ſo rude, as doth appear)
Hope to endure, ſith workes of heavenly wits
Are quite devour'd, and brought to nought by little bits!

Thus Chaucer.

> This old ſtorie in latine, which I finde
> Of queen Annelida, and falſe Arcite,
> That Elde, which all thingis can frete and bite,
> (And it hath freten many a noble ſtorie)
> Hath nigh devourid out of her memorie *.
>
> B. vi. c. ix. ſ. v.

He chaunc't to ſpy a ſort of ſhepheard groomes
Playing on pipes, and caroling apace,
The whiles their beaſts, there in the budded broomes,
Beſide them fed. — — — —

Theſe verſes are a diſtant imitation of Chaucer. They are more immediately an imitation of himſelf in the Eclogues.

So loytering live you little heard-groomes,
Keeping your beaſts in the budded broomes:
* * * * * * * *
And crowing in pipes made of grene corne †.

* Of Q. Annelid. and falſe Arcite. v. 10. † Februarie.

which are apparently an immediate imitation of thefe in Chaucer.

> And many a floite, and litlyng horne,
> And pipis made of grene corne.
> As have thefe little herdegromes,
> That keepen beaftis in the bromes*.

The word *herd-groome* occurs again in AUGUST.

> — — Yonder *herd-groome* and none other.

And again in the poem before us.

> — — That they were poore *heard-groomes*.
>
> 6. 11. 39.

B. vii. c. vii. f. v.

> Then forth iffew'd (great goddeffe) dame NATURE,
> With goodly port, and gracious majefty,
> Being far greater, and more tall of ftature
> Than any of the gods, or powers on hie.

Afterwards, fpeaking of her face. ft. 6.

> — — — It fo beauteous was,
> And round about fuch beames of fplendor threw,
> That it the funne a thoufand times did pafs,
> Ne could be feene, but like an image in a glafs.

* Houfe of Fame. v. 133.

vii.

That well may feemen true: for well I weene
That this fame day, when fhe on Arlo fat,
Her garment was fo bright, and wondrous fheene,
That my fraile wit cannot devize to what
It to compare, &c.

viii.

In a fair plaine, upon an equall hill,
She placed was in a pavilion;
Not fuch as craftes-men by their idle fkill,
Are wont for princes ftate to fafhion;
But th' earth herfelf of her owne motion,
Out of her fruitfull bofome made to grow
Moft dainty trees, that fhooting up anon
Did feem to bowe their bloofming heads full lowe;
Fit homage unto her, and like a throne did fhew.

ix.

So hard it is for any living wight,
All her array, and veftiments to tell,
That old Dan Geffrey (in whofe gentle fpright
The pure well-head of poefie did dwell)
In his FOWLES PARLEY durft not with it mell,
But it transfer'd to Alane, who, he thought,
Had in his * *plaint of kindes* defcrib'd it well.
* * * * * * *

* Planctus Naturæ.

The

The ninth stanza is no obscure hint, that our poet had been consulting Chaucer's *Assembly of fowles* for this description of NATURE. But Spenser has given many new and delicate touches to Chaucer's rough sketch, as will appear upon comparison.

> Tho' was I ware, where there ysate a quene,
> That as of light the sommer sonne shene
> Passith the sterre, right so ovir mesure,
> She fairer was than any other creture.
> And in a launde, upon a hill of floures,
> Was set this quene, this noble goddesse NATURE,
> Of branchis were her hallis and her boures,
> Irought aftir her craft and her mesure.
> * * * * * * * * *
> And right as Alaine in the plaint of kinde
> Deviseth Nature of soche araie and face,
> In such araie men mighten her there finde *.

B. xvii. c. viii. s. xlvi.

> But Life was like a faire young lusty boy,
> Such as they faine Dan Cupid to have beene,
> Full of delightfull health, and lively joy,
> Deckt all with flowres, and wings of gold fit to employ.

Chaucer thus represents Cupid.

* Assemblie of Fowles, v. 298.

But of his robe to devife
I dread encumbred for to be;
For not yclad in filk was he
But all in floures, and flourettes *.

But the antients have left us no authority for fuch a reprefentation of Cupid. Our author, ft. 34. above, gives him a green veft.

And Cupid-felfe about her fluttred all in greene.

Which is equally unwarrantable. Though Catullus has given him a yellow veft.

Quam circumcurfans huc illuc fæpe Cupido,
 Fulgebat CROCINA *candidus in tunica* †.

Where Scaliger remarks from Julius Pollux, that Sappho attributes a purple veft to this deity; but according to the general fenfe in which πορφυρῶ is sometimes ufed, fhe may probably mean a *rich* mantle.

B. vii. c. viii. f. xl.

Next was November: he full groffe and fat,
As fed with lard, and that right well might feeme,
For he had been a fatting hogs of late.
* * * * * * * *

---

* Romaunt of the Rofe. v. 890. † Ad Manlium.

xli.

And after him came next the chill December;
Yet he thro' merry feasting which he made,
And great bonfires, did not the cold remember,
His Saviour's birth his mind so much did glad.
* * * * * * * * * *
And in his hand a broad deep boawle he beares,
Of which he freely drinks an health to all his peeres.

In describing these figures, Spenser seems to have remembered some circumstances in Chaucer's picture of Janus, or JANUARY.

Janus sit by the fire with double berde,
And drinketh of his bugle horne the wine;
Before him stant brawn of the tuskid swine,
And * nowil singeth every lustie man †.

I shall now lay before the reader some instances of phrases and words, which Spenser has adopted from Chaucer.

B. i. *Introduction*, st. iii.

— — With you bring triumphant MART.

We have no reason to imagine, that Spenser here arbitrarily uses MART instead of *Mars*, for the convenience of rhyme, since he had the authority of Chaucer.

* i. e. *Christmas*.   † Frankelein's tale. v. 2808.

All

All efily now for the love of MARTE *.

Again,

O cruil god of deth, defpiteous MARTE †.

We find it likewife in other places. Chaucer fometimes ufes MART for *war*.

B. i. c. i. f. xxxiv.

And well could FILE his tongue as fmooth as glafs.

So Chaucer.

For wele he wifte when the fong was fonge,
He muft preche, and well AFILE his tonge ‡.

Again,

This Pandarus gan new his tong AFILE §.

The fame metaphor occurs again in our author.

His practick wit, and his fair FILED tongue.

2. 1. 3.

— — — — However, fir, ye FILE
Your courteous tongue his praifes to compile.

3. 2. 12.

It is found in Skelton's *Boke of Colin Cloute*.

But they their tongues did FILE
And make a pleafaunte ftyle.

* Tr. and Cr. b. 2. v. 988.   † Ibid. b. 2. v. 435.   ‡ Prol. 713.   § Tr. and Cr. b. 1. v. 1681.

And in other passages of the same author.

In *Colin Clouts come home againe*, it is joined with it's literal meaning.

A FILED tongue, *furnish'd with termes of art.*

It seems at length to have grown into a common phrase. Thus Holofernes in Shakespeare: "His hu-"mour is lofty; his discourse peremptory, his *tongue* "FILED *."

And Jonson.

For he's both noble, lovely, young,
And for the troubled client FILES his tongue:
Child of a thousand arts, &c †.

B. i. c. iv. f. xl.

Reboubted battaile ready to DARRAINE.

DARRAINE is often used by Chaucer.

That everich should an hundred knights bring
The battle to DARRAIN ‡.

Full privily two harneis had he dight
Both sufficient and mete to DARRAINE
The battail in the field, betwixt them twaine §.

* Love's Labour Lost. act i. sc. 1.   † Hor. b. iv. od. 1.
‡ Knight's tale, v. 2098.   § Ibid. v. 1632.

The

The word seems to be derived from the french *arranger*; so that to DARRAINE BATTLE is, *to set the battle in array.* Our poet has used ARRANGED, from *arranger*, and applied it to battle, more than once.

> So both to battel fierce ARRANGED are.   1. 2. 36.
>
> — — — ARRANG'D in battle new.   1. 6. 38.

Chaucer, in another place, uses DARRAINE in a sense not agreeable to its genuine signification.

> Everich of you shall bring an hundred knights
> * * * * * * * * * *
> Alredy to DARRAIN here by battaile*.

Where it should imply, *to determine.*

This word being a Chaucerism, our author has very remarkably affected the use of it, viz.

> — — Sad battaile to DARRAINE.   1. 7. 11,
>
> — — — — — To DARRAINE
> A triple warre. — — — —   2. 2. 26.
>
> — — Six knights that did DARRAINE
> Fierce battaile against one. — —   3. 1. 20.
>
> — — New battaile to DARRAINE.   4. 4. 26.

* Ibib. 1583.

— New

— — New battaile to DARRAINE. 4. 5. 24.

And dreadfull battle 'twixt them do DARRAINE.
5. 2. 15.

In which they two the combat might DARRAINE.
6. 12. 9.

— Those giants, which did war DARRAINE
Against the heavens. — — — 6. 7. 41.

We have here an instance in which the word is used in a more vague sense,

— — How best he might DARRAINE
That enterprize. — — — — 4. 9. 4.

But we are told, in the glossary to Chaucer [*], that this word, among other senses, signifies, *to dare, to attempt*. Thus, by a gradual detortion, and by an imperceptible progression from one kindred sense to another, words at length attain a meaning entirely foreign to their original etymology.

Spenser's frequent use of DARRAINE seems to have somewhat familiarised it in Queen Elizabeth's age. We meet with it in Shakespeare, who probably drew it from our author.

DARRAIGN your battle; they are near at hand [†].

[*] Urry's Edit.   [†] Third Part of Hen. vi. act. 2. f. 3.

B. i.

B. i. c. vii. f. xxix.

His GLITTERAND armor shined far away.

Spenser thus affectedly spells the participle *glittering*, in imitation of Chaucer.

So in the *Plowman's Tale*,

> That high on horse willeth ride
> In GLITTERANDE gold, of great array*.

And in the same poem,

> With GLITTERANDE gold as green as gall †.

GLITTERAND is very frequently used by our author.

> Soone as those GLITTERAND armes he did espy.
> 2. 7. 42.
> Eftsoones himselfe in GLITTERANDE arms he dight.
> 2. 11. 17.
> Her glorious GLITTERAND light doth all mens eyes amaze.   1. 4. 16.

We meet with it likewise in the Eclogues.

> Ygirt with bells of GLITTERAND gold ‡.

Many of Chaucer's active participles are thus terminated, viz. *sittande*, *smertande*, *laughande*, &c. for sit-

---

* Ver. 2073.   † Ver. 2103.   ‡ July.

ting,

ting, smarting, laughing. We meet with this termination of the active participle very frequently in the antient Scotch poets.

B. i. c. vii. f. xiv.

— — — — — Do him to die.

Chaucer,

— — — — — And doen to die
Thefe lofengeours, with her flatterie *.

The inftances of this expreffion are innumerable, both in Chaucer, and in our author. This is, *Je lui ferai mourir*, Fr. *farollo morire*, Ital.

B. ii. c. ii. f. xxii.

And fuffred not their blowes to BITE him nere.

Again,

— His rebuke which BIT her neare. 6. 11. 64.

In Mother *Hubbard's Tale*.

—— —— Spight BITES neare.

In Shakefpeare,

—— —— —— Thou bitter fky,
Thou doft not BITE fo nigh †.

* Rom. Rofe. v. 1061. † As you like it, act ii, f. 10.

That

That is to *pierce to the quick.*

BITE is frequently used in the sense, to *pierce*, or *wound*, in Chaucer.

>Ne short sword to stick with point BITING
>No man ne draw *.

>And made his sword deep in his flesh YBITE †.

>The jealous strokes on their helmes BITE ‡.

Speaking of a sword, afterwards,

>Throughout his armure it will *kerve* and BITE.

>But in his sleve he gan to thring
>A rasour sharpe and *well*-BITING §.

Nor are instances of this word, used simply for *wound* or *pierce*, less frequent in Spenser, viz.

>The cruell steele so greedily doth BITE
>In tender flesh. ———   ———   1. 5. 9.

>His BITING sword, and his devouring speare.
>   1. 7. 48.

>That first did teach the cursed steele to BITE
>In his own flesh. ———   ———   2. 6. 32.

* Knight's Tale, 2548.   † Ibid. 2642.   ‡ Ibid. 2636.
§ Rom. Rose, v. 7319.

The pointed fteele —— ——
His harder hide would neither *pearce* nor BITE.
1. 11. 16.

—— The fharpe fteele arriving forcibly
On his broad fhield, BIT not. —— 2. 5. 4.

A ftroke,
And glauncing downe, would not his owner BITE.
2. 8. 38.

And *pearced* to the fkin, but BIT not more.
2. 8. 44.

A dart,
And had not powre in his foft flefh to BITE.
3. 5. 19.

Till on her horfes hinder parts it fell,
Where BITING deep, fo deadly it impreft.
4. 6. 13.

That glauncing on her fhoulder-plate it BIT
Unto the bone. —— —— —— 5. 7. 33.

But BYTING deepe therein. —— 6. 12. 21.

i. e. into his fhield.

The tempred fteele did not into his braine-pan BITE.
6. 6. 30.

Shakefpeare has ufed BITE fimply, for *wound*.
" *Nym.* I fhould have borne the humoured letter to
" her: but I have a fword, and it fhall BITE, upon
" my

" my neceffity *." The meaning is, *I have a fword, and, it fhall* wound *when my need or neceffity requires.* This interpretation of BITE, from Chaucer and Spenfer, which Theobald feems to have been unacquainted with, plainly fhews the propriety of placing a comma after BITE, which the learned bifhop of Glocefter, [Dr. Warburton] has done with his ufual fagacity.

B. ii. c. iv. f. xxiv.

Saying, he now had boulted all the floure.

That is, *he had fearched the matter to the bottom.* This form is founded upon an old proverb in Chaucer,

> But I ne cannot *boult it to the brenne,*
> As can that holy doctour faint Auften †.

B. ii. c. vi. f. xliii.

HARROW now out, and *weal-away,* he cryde.

So Chaucer,

> And gan to cry HARROW and *weal-away* ‡.

HARO is a form of exclamation antiently ufed in Normandy, to call for help, or to raife the *Hue and Cry* §. We find it again in our author,

---

* Merry Wives of Windfor, act. 2, fc. 3. † Nonne's Prieft's Tale, 1355. ‡ Reve's Tale, 964. § Gloffary to Urry's edit.

HARROW the flames which me confume. —
2. 6. 49.
Again,
— — HARROW, and *weal-away!*
After fo wicked deed, &c. — — 2. 8. 46.

It occurs often in Chaucer, and is, I think, always ufed as an exclamation of GRIEF; but there are fome paffages in an old MYSTERY printed at Paris, 1541, where it is applied as a term of ALARM, according to it's original ufage. Lucifer is introduced fummoning the devils.

Dyables mefchans, &c.
* * * * * * * *
Viendrez vous point a mes cris, et aboys,
* * * * * * * *
HARO, HARO, *nui de vous je ne veoys?*

And in another place, where he particularly addreffes Belial.

HARO, HARO, *approche toy grand dyable,*
Approche toy notayre mal fiable,
Fier Belial, &c.

It is obfervable, that the permiffion of the CLAMEUR DE HARO is to this day fpecified, among that of other officers, in the inftrument of Licence prefixed to books printed in France.

B. iii.

(173)

B. iii. c. i. f. lxiv.

To ftir up ftrife, and troublous CONTECK broche.

Spenfer here, when he might have ufed *conteft*, chufes rather Chaucer's obfolete term CONTECK.

Thus in the *Knight's Tale*.

CONTEKE with bloody knyves, and fharpe menace *.

Again,

Of CONTEKE, and of whelpis gret and light †.

Our poet had ufed it before in SEPTEMBER.

But kindle coales of CONTECKE and ire,
Wherewith they fett all the world on fire.

In MAY,

So CONTECKE foon by concord might be ended.

CONTECKE occurs often in Gafcoigne.

B. iii. c. ii. f. v.

— — Like a PINED ghoft. — —

So likewife,

That like a PINED ghoft he foon appears. 4. 7. 41.

* Ver. 2006. † Nonne's Prieft's Tale, v. 10047.

We

We find FORPYNED *ghoſt* in Chaucer, which is the same as PYNED *ghoſt*.

<blockquote>He was not pale as a FORPYNED ghoſt *.

B. iii. C. vi. ſ. vi.</blockquote>

<blockquote>But wondrouſly they were begot and bred,
Through influence of th' heavens chearfull ray;
As it in antique books is mentioned.</blockquote>

Theſe introductions give authority to a fictitious ſtory. Thus the tale of Canace is uſhered in,

<blockquote>Whylom as antique ſtories tellen us.   4. 2. 32.</blockquote>

And, in another place, he refers to hiſtory for a ſanction to his invention,

<blockquote>As ye may elſe-where read that ruefull hiſtory.
3. 6. 53.</blockquote>

Chaucer frequently makes uſe of theſe forms.

He thus begins the *Knight's Tale*.

<blockquote>Whylom as olde ſtoris tellin us.</blockquote>

And again, in the ſame Tale,

<blockquote>— — — As old books us ſaine,
That all this ſtorie tellen more plaine †.</blockquote>

* Prolog. v. 205.   † Knight's Tale, v. 1466.

And afterwards,

— — — As men may behold
In Stace of Thebes, and these bookes old *.

The Siege of Thebes, and the Destruction of Troy, were the two favorite classical stories of the dark ages. The characters and incidents of these they were mixing perpetually with their romances. Thus, in Chaucer's *Palamon* and *Arcite*, a turnament is celebrated before Theseus. Sir Palomydes, one of the knights of Arthur's round table, is only a corruption from Palamedes, a famous grecian leader. Chaucer † mentions Sir Tristram with Achilles. He also joins Virgil's trumpeter Misenus with those famous martial musicians of the Turney, who " usid the clarion" in the many celebrated feats of chivalry performed in Catalonia and Arragon ‡. Perceforest, in his romance, says, " *Si j' avois autant de possessions comme avoit le* " *roi Alexandre, et de sens comme le sage Solomon, et* " *de* chevalerie *comme eut le preux* HECTOR DE " TROYE, &c. §. But examples are innumerable. The story of Troy they first got from Dares Phrygius, and Dictys Cretensis; for Dante never had read Ho-

* Knight's Tale, v. 2295. † Assemb. of Fowles, 290.
‡ House of Fame, 3, 153.
§ Perceforest, tom. ii. fol. 121. *verso.* col. 1. 2.

mer,

mer, and Boccace was the first who introduced him into Italy. In the library of Glastonbury abbey, A.D. 1248, we find a book entitled, *Excidium Trojæ* *. But much earlier than this, in an age of grosser ignorance, so popular and respectable was the story of Troy, that Witlafius, a king of the West-Saxons, A. D. 833. grants in his charter, among other things, to the church of Croyland abbey, his robe of tissue, on which was embroidered the *destruction of Troy*. This was to be hung against the walls of the choir, on the day of his anniversary †.

The story of the golden fleece, was likewise held in high reverence, and frequently furnished heroes and heroines for their legends. Chaucer often mentions *Duke* Jason, and *Queen* Medea ‡. I have seen the *Historie of the Knight Jason*, by Gerard de Leew ||, fol. Andewarp, [*Antwerp*] 1480. About the same time, Caxton printed *The Historie of Jason; towchynge the conqueste of the golden fleece*. This book was trans-

---

* Hearn, Catal. Johan. Glaston. vol. 2. p. 435.
† Rerum Anglic. Script. vet. Oxon. 1684. tom. 1. *Hist*. Ingulphi, p. 9.
‡ Skelton says, *in the boke of Philipe Sparrowe*, pag. 233. ed. 1738.
    I can tell a *greate peece*,
    Of the golden flece,
    How *Jason* it wan.
|| Who wrote also *the Chronycles of the reame of Englonde, with their apperteignaunces*.

Jason's

lated from the french of Raoul le Feure, chaplain to the famous duke of Burgundy, who, in memory of Jason's expedition, but perhaps more immediately from the popularity of the story at that time, founded the order of the Golden Fleece, the first chapter of which was held, 1468. Caxton, in his Prologue, mentions a stately chamber, in the duke's castle at Hesdin in Artois, sumptuously adorned with paintings, perhaps with tapestry, of this story, and furnished moreover with a curious piece of machinery, by which the magical powers of Medea were represented in the sudden production of snow, rain, lightning, and thunder. " Well wote I, says he, that the noble duc Philippe, " first founder of this said order, did doo make *a cham-* " *bre* in the castell of Hesdyn, wherein was *craftyly and* " *curyously depeynted the conqueste of the Golden Fleece,* by " the said Jason. In which chambre I have been, " and seen the sayd historie so depeynted; and in re- " membraunce of Medea, and *her cunning and science,* " he had doo make in the sayd chambre, by *subtill* " *engyne,* that, when it he wold, it shulde seeme, " that it lightned, and after, thondre, snowe, and " rayne, *and all within the sayd chambre,* as aft times, " and when it shulde please him, which was all made " for his singuler plaisir." But afterwards, by the advice of John German, bishop of Nevers, first chancellor

A a

cellor of this order, Jason's fleece was exchanged for Gideon's; and the story of the latter was wrought into rich hangings of gold and silver, which were remaining in the court of Bruffels, when Chifletius published his account of this inftitution*.

Few ftories of antiquity have more the caft of one of the old romances than this of Jason. An expedition of a new kind is made into a ftrange and diftant country, attended with infinite dangers and difficulties. The king's daughter of the new country, is an enchantrefs; fhe falls in love with the young prince, who is the chief adventurer. The prize which he feeks, is guarded by brazen-footed bulls, who breathe fire; and by a hideous dragon, who never fleeps. The princefs lends him the affiftance of her charmes and incantations, to conquer thefe obftacles; fhe gives him poffeffion of the prize, leaves her father's court, and follows the young prince into his native country. It fhould be obferved, that thefe wonders fubfifted in that part of the world, from which, in after ages, we fetched all our romantic fictions. Homer has his giants, and other incidents of romance, fcattered in different parts of the Iliad and Odyffey, particularly the latter: but fuch incidents are here

* Breviarum Velleris aurei.

found

found in the aggregate, and form a series of romantic adventures.

B. iii. c. vii. f. xlvii.

———— The mightie OLLYPHAUNT that wrote
Great wrecke to manie errant knights of yore.

The giant OLLYPHANT here mentioned, is probably the same which Sir Thopas encounters in his expedition to the land of FAIRY.

Till him there came a great gyaunt,
His name was called Sir OLLYPHAUNT *.

B. iii. c. viii. f. lvii.

Becaufe I could not give her many a jane.

So Chaucer,

Of Bruges were his hofin brown,
His robe was of Chekelatoun,
That coft many a JANE †.

Many a JANE, i. e. " much money." Skinner informs us, that JANE is a *coin of Genoa*; and Speght, in his Gloffary to Chaucer, interprets JANE, *half-pence of Janua,* [Genoa] or *galy half-pence.*

* Rime of Sir Topas, v. 3315.   † Ibid. 3242.

Chaucer sometimes uses it as a coin of little value; as,

Dear enough a JANE *.

And in other places.

Stow has given us an account of these GALY HALF-PENCE at large. " In this lane, [Minchin] dwelled
" divers ftrangers, born of Genoa, and those partes;
" these were commonly called gallie men, as men
" that came up in the gallies, who brought up wines
" and other merchandizes, which they landed in
" Thames-ftrete, at a place called galley-key: they
" had a certain coyne of filver amongft themfelves,
" which were half-pence of Genoa, and were called
" GALLEY HALF-PENCE. These half-pence were
" forbidden in the thirteenth year of Henry IV, and
" again by parliament in the third of Henry V, by
" the name of half-pence of Genoa, forbidden to
" paffe as unlawfull payment amongft the Englifh
" fubjects. Notwithftanding, in my youth, I have
" feen them paffe currant, &c †." This paffage will serve to illuftrate Speght's interpretation of the word under confideration, which is at prefent obfcure and unfatisfactory.

* Cl. of Oxenford's Tale, ver. 2020.
† Survey of London, pag. 97. edit. 1599. quarto.

B. iii.

B. iii. c. ix. f. iii.

Then liften lordinges. ——— ———

Chaucer often applies this introductory form in the *Canterbury Tales.* Thus too, the old poem of *Sir Bevis of Southampton* begins.

> *Liften* LORDINGES, and hold you ftill,
> Of doutie men tell you I will.

And Robert Brunne in the fame manner begins the Prologue to his Chronicle *.

> LORDINGES, that be now here,
> If you will liften and lere,
> All the ftory of Inglande.

This addrefs to the LORDINGES, requefting their filence and attention, is a manifeft indication that thefe antient pieces were originally fung to the harp, or recited before grand affemblies, upon folemn occafions.

B. iii. c. ix. f. xx.

> Her golden lockes, that were in tramels gay
> Upbounden, did themfelves adowne difplay,
> And raught unto her heeles. ———

* Ed. Hearn, vol. 1. p. 96.

So Chaucer,

> Her tresses yellow, and long straughten,
> Unto her heeles downe they raughten [*].

And in the same poem,

> Her haire downe to her heeles went [†].

Our author again expresses himself in the same manner, speaking of a robe.

> —— When she lift, it raught
> Down to her lowest heele. ——
>
> 5. 5. 2.

Also,

> —— Her golden lockes that were upbound
> Still in a knott, unto her heeles downe traced.
>
> 4. 1. 13.

This mention of *golden hair* puts me in mind of a correction which Mr. Upton has made in the following verse of Chaucer.

> Her GILDED heris with a GOLDEN thread
> Iboundin were [‡].

Mr. Upton [§] supposes that here is a transposition occasioned by the transcriber's haste, and that we should apply *gilded* to *threde*, and *goldin* to *heris*, viz.

[*] Rom. Rose, v. 1021.   [†] Ibid. 1218.   [‡] Assemble of Fowles, v. 267.   [§] Letter to G. West, Esq; p. 35.

Her

Her *goldin* heris with a *gilded* threde
Iboundin were. ——— ———

The alteration appears at first sight to be very just; but it is perhaps unnecessary, if we consider, that *gilte*, or *gilded*, is often used by Chaucer, and applied to *hair*.
Thus,
His GILT *here* was ycrounid with a son *.

And in the same poem,
Hide Absolon thy GILTE *tressis* clere †.

We have here *gilded hair*,
Dischevilid with her bright GILDID *here* ‡.

B. iii. c. ix. f. xxxi.
——— ——— Thus was the ape
By their faire handling put into Malbecco's cape.

A proverb from Chaucer.
This cursed Chanon *put in his hode an ape* §.
Again,
The Monke *put* in the marchants *hode an ape* ‖.

---

* Leg. of G. Women, v. 230. † Ibid. v. 249. ‡ Ibid. v. 390. § Host's Words, chan. Y. v. 1510. ‖ Host's Words, ship. 2948.

B. iii.

B. iii. c. x. f. xix.

To feek her ENDLONG both by fea and land.

I do not remember that ENDLONG occurs in any poet before Spenfer, Chaucer excepted; nor in any of Spenfer's contemporaries; fo that probably our author drew it from his favorite bard, viz.

—— —— The red blood
Ran ENDLONG the tree*.

Alfo,
 Loke what daye that ENDLONG to Britaine,
 Ye remeve all thefe rockis ftone by ftone †.

And in other places.

Pope has revived this word with great propriety.

B. iii. c. x. f. xxxi.

Bigge looking, like a doutie DOUZEPERE.

Dofeperis, in Chaucer, is from the french, *les douze pairs*; the twelve peers of France. Some legendary governors of Rome are fo called in allufion to thofe of France, in thefe verfes of the *Marchant's Tale*, or *Hiftory of Beryn*.

* Squire's Tale, v. 435.   † Fran. Tale, v. 2538.

When

(185)

When it [Rome] was governed by the DOSEPERIS *.

Then Conſtantyne the third after theſe DOSIPERIS †.

We find *douze-piers* in Caxton's *Godfrey of Boloyne* ‡. It occurs likewiſe in Brunne's Chronicle, finiſhed in 1338 §.

> The twelve *duzperis* of price ‖,
> Departid the land in twelve parties.

Again,

> In France was twelve lord fers
> That men cald *duze pers*.

In the Chronicle of Robert of Gloceſter, they are called *dozperes*. In Jeffery of Monmouth, *twelve conſuls*. In the old romance written by Gualter d'Avignon, *les douze compagnons*.

> *Aſſez de mal me fit votre oncle Ganilion*,
> *Qui trahit en Eſpaigne* les douze compagnons (*).

Cervantes ſuppoſes, that a romance entitled the *Twelve Peers of France*, written by Turpin, from which Boyardo borrowed many fictions, was diſcovered among others in Don Quixote's library (†).

---

* Ver. 44.   † Ver. 51.   ‡ In the Proheme.   § Langtoft's *Chronicle*, as improved and illuſtrated by R. Brunne. ed. T. Hearn, Oxon. 1725. ut ſupr.   ‖ *Forte* Legend. Paris.   (*) Fauchet des Dignities, liv. 2.   (†) Part 1.

B b   The

The knight afterwards miftakes himfelf for the *twelve peers*, and the curate for archbifhop Turpin. " Truly " my lord archbifhop, it is a great difhonour to us, " that are called the *twelve peers of France*, to permit " the knights of the court thus to bear away the glory " of the turnament *." I have feen a very antient fpanifh romance, in verfe, entitled, " *El verdarero* " *fucefo de la famofa* Battallo de Ronfcevalles †; *con la* " Muerte *de les* Doze Peres de Francia." But I do not remember, that *douzepere* is ufed in the fingular number, in our author's fenfe, except in Skelton.

This daungerous DOWSIPERE ‡.

A late french writer, in a Memoir on the *Origin of Chivalry and Romances* §, endeavours to prove, that the knights of Arthur's round table were feigned in imitation of Charlemagne's twelve peers ‖; and that the englifh, jealous of the glory of the french, and defirous of adorning their hiftory with a prince equal

* Ch. 6. ch. 7.
† The ballad of Ronfcevalles is a common fong in Spain.
‡ Edit. 1736. pag. 16.
§ Sur l'Origine de l'ancienne Chevalerie, &c. Hiftoire de l'Acad. des Infcript. &c. tom. 23. pag. 236. a Paris, 1756. 4to.
‖ Many writers attribute thefe twelve peers to our Arthur. Others to Hugh Capet, and King Robert, circ. 1000. But they feem more immediately to belong to Charlemagne.

to

to the boasted Charlemagne of their neighbours, formed their accomplished Arthur upon the same plan. " Il est donc très vraisemblable, que toute l'histoire " d'Artus s'est formée sur celle de Charlemagne; " que le regne de ce dernier prince a été la source " de toutes les idées romanesque, qui ont germé dans " les siécles suivans." He adds, among other supposed circumstances of correspondence, that Gawaine, Arthur's nephew, is Charlemagne's nephew, the renowned Roland. But this hypothesis is perhaps more specious than true. However, he allows, that our History of Jeffery of Monmouth is the original of the old french romance entitled *Brut:* " Maitre Huista- " ches, auteur de *Brut*, n'est que le copiste et l'am- " plificateur de Geoffroi de Monmouth."

Milton alludes to these *twelve peers* more than once. Speaking of Angelica,

— — Sought by many prowest knights,
Both paynim, and the *peers* of Charlemayne*.

That is, in a confined sense, the *twelve peers* of Charlemagne. And in the following passage, by Charlemagne's *peerage*, he does not mean his peers or nobles in a general sense, but the *twelve peers*, his established guard, and constant attendants in all his expeditions.

* Paradise Regained, b. 3. v. 335.

Or whom Biferta sent from Afric shore,
When *Charlemaine*, with all his *peerage* fell
By Fontarabbia *. — — — —

It has been mentioned as an *extraordinary* circumstance, that Milton was a great reader of romances in his youth. But this is no more than what was common, in some degree, to his cotemporaries. Before the grand Rebellion, these books were in all hands; and were the source from which young readers especially, in the age of fiction and fancy, *nourished the* SUBLIME. I own indeed, that Milton's strong imagination might receive peculiar impressions from this sort of reading.

B. iii. c. xii. s. xi.

With him went DANGER. —— ——

Spenser seems to have personified *danger* after the example of Chaucer, who has made him a very significant character in the *Romaunt of the Rose*; but I do not remember that any circumstances in Spenser's description of him are borrowed from thence. He is again introduced as the guardian of the gate of *good desert*, in the temple of Venus, 4. 10. 18. and afterwards, as an advocate for Duessa, 5. 9. 35.

* Paradise Lost, b. 1. v. 584.

Danger

Danger is alfo a perfonage in Skelton's *Bouge of Court.*

B. iv. c. i. f. xxxii.

His name was BLANDAMOUR. — —

There was an old romance which celebrated the atchievements of BLANDAMOUR; which Spenfer might have feen. If he had not, he probably drew the name from this hint of Chaucer,

> Men fpeken of romances of pris,
> Of Horne-child, and Ipotis,
> Of Bevis, and Sir Gie,
> Of Sir * Libeaux, and BLANDAMOURE †.

B. iv. c. iv. f. xxiii.

— — — Fiercely forth he rode,
Like fparke of fire, that from the anvil GLODE.

The compiler of the Gloffary to Spenfer informs us, that GLODE fignifies *glanced,* or that it is written, by poetical licence, for *glowed.* As to the latter of thefe explanations, I do not think, that *glow* had ac-

---

* He is fometimes called Sir Libius;
    And of *Syr Libius,*
    Named Diofconius.   Skelton, p. 233. ed. 1738.
His Legend is ftill extant.

† Rime of Sir Thopas, v. 3402.

quired

quired fo vague a fenfe in our author's age; and where is the proof or authority for the former? Spenfer undoubtedly borrowed it from the following paſſage of Chaucer.

>His good ſteede he beſtrode
>And forth upon his way GLODE
>   As ſparke out of the bronde*.

Our author has here plainly borrowed the thought, as well as the particular word in queſtion, which, however, he has differently applied. May not GLODE be the preter-imperfect tenfe of *glide?*

Gower has uſed this word in the fame manner, and moſt beautifully. He is fpeaking of Medea, going out at midnight to gather herbs for her incantations.

>Thus it befell upon a night,
>Whann there was nought but ſterre light,
>She was vaniſhed right as hir liſt,
>That no wight but hirfelfe wiſt:
>And that was at midnight tide,
>The world was ſtill on every ſide,
>With open head, and foote all bare,
>Hir heare to fprad; ſhe gan to fare:

* Rime of Sir Thopas, v. 3408.

Upon hir clothes gyrte fhe was,
And *fpecheles, upon the gras*
She GLODE *forth, as an adder doth* *.

B. v. c. i. f. xxv.

— — This doubtfull caufes right
Can hardly but by facrament be tride,
Or elfe by ordele.

So Chaucer,

Where fo you lift by ordal, or by othe ‡.

Sacrament is the oath of purgation.

B. vi. c. vi. f. xii.

'Gainft all both good and bad, both MOST and LEAST.

MOST here fignifies *greateft*; and in the following inftances; as, MORE implies *greater*.

I do poffeffe the world's MOST regiment. 7. 7. 17.

That is, I am poffeffed of the greateft fway over the world.

— — All other weapons *leffe* or MORE,
Which warlike ufes had devis'd of yore. 5. 8. 34.

For ere thou limit what is *leffe* or MORE. 5. 2. 34.

* Confeffio Amantis, l. v. fol. 105. edit. Berthelette, 1554. fol.
‡ Tr. and Cr. b. 3. v. 1048.

In *Sonnet* 20.

  In his MOST pride difdaineth, &c.

Again,

  What though the fea with waves continuall
  Doe eat the earth, it is no MORE at all,
  Ne is the earth the *leſſe*. — — 5. 2. 39.

 In *Sonnet* 55.

  Thus for the world's MOST ornament.

Many other paſſages might be brought from Spenſer.

 This is the language of Chaucer; VIZ.

  I faie, that ſhe ne had not MOST fairneſſe*.

That is, I do not affirm ſhe had the *greateſt* ſhare of beauty.

  The grete geſtes alſo to the MOST and LESTE †.

Again,

  From Boloigne is the erle of Pavie come,
  Of which the fame yſpronge to MOST and LESTE ‡.

Thus we have alſo MUCH or LESS for *greater* and *ſmaller*.

 * Monk's Tale, ver. 367. † Knight's Tale, ver. 2200.
 ‡ Cl. of Oxenford's Tale, v. 1900.   Both

Both of the fee, and rivers MORE and LESSE §.

Thus also MUCH or LITE is *great* and *small*.

> But he ne left, neither for raine ne thonder,
> In fickenefs, ne in mifchief to vifite
> The farthift in his parifh MUCH or LITE ‖.

And to this day MUCH is prefixed to fome villages in England, as a mark of greatnefs. The ingenious author of *Mifcellaneous Obfervations on Mackbeth*, remarks, that in the interpolated Mandeville, a book printed in the age of queen Elizabeth, there is a chapter, *Of India*, THE MORE AND THE LESS*.

I had almoft paffed over fome of the fubfequent inftances.

> B. ii. c. vi. f. xxix.

That a large purple ftreame adowne their GIAMBEUX falls.

He probably drew GIAMBEUX, i. e. *boots*, from this paffage in the *Rime of Sir Topas*.

> His JAMBEUX were of cure buly †.

Which line is more french than englifh.

§ Frank. Tale, ver. 2600. ‖ Prol. ver. 494.
* Note 43. † Ver. 3380.

Ses JAMBEUX *etoient de cuir bouilli.*

i. e. " His boots were made of tanned leather."

B. vi. c. vii. f. xliii.

But in a jacket quilted richly rare
Upon CHECKLATOUN, he was ftrangely dight.

CHECKLATOUN likewife occurs in the laſt mentioned poem of Chaucer.

His robe was of CHEKELATOUN ‡.

Speght * interprets this word *a ſtuff of checkerwork made of cloth of gold.* Skinner, *a ſtuff of motley.* But our author, in his *View of the State of Ireland,* has given us a more fatisfactory explication of this word, as he found it in the fame paffage of Chaucer. " The " quilted leather jack is old englifh : For it was the " proper weed of the horfeman, as you may read in " Chaucer, when he defcribeth *Sir Thopas's apparel,* " *and armour, as he went to fight againſt the gyant, in* " *his robe of* CHECKLATOUN, which is that kind of " *gilded leather* with which they ufe to *embroider* their " irifh jackets."

To PRICK is very frequently ufed by Spenfer, as well as by Chaucer, for, *to ride*; as is MANY for *re-*

‡ Ver. 5243.   * Gloff. Chaucer.

tinue,

tinue, multitude, or *company.* Dryden, in his inimitable music-ode, has thus used MANY.

The MANY rend the skies with loud applause.

Many also is to be found with this sense in Harrington, Shakespeare, &c.

It should not be omitted, that LAD for *led,* often occurs in Chaucer; as it does likewise in Spenser, viz. a milk-white lamb she LAD. 1. 1. 4. whom they LAD. 2. 12. 84. a wretched life they LAD. 4. 8. 2. to their purpose LAD. 5. 12. 37. the virgin LAD. 4. 12. 33. he him LAD. 5. 1. 22. away was LAD. 6. 10. 39.

Our author seems to have used, *never none,* for, *there never was one,* from an affectation of Chaucer's manner; although it must be confessed, that most of our old english writers frequently join two negatives, when no affirmation is intended. Hickes, after observing that a negation is often expressed in the anglo-saxonic by two negatives, has these words. "Editor "*Chauceri nihil antiqui sapiens*, dicit, ipsum imitatum*

---

* "It is his manner likewise, imitating the Greekes, by two nega-"tives, to cause a greater negation; as, *I ne said none ill.*" Speght's ADVERTISEMENT TO THE READERS; prefixed to his second edition of Chaucer's works; London, *printed by Adam Islip,* 1602. . . . . But the labours of this editor deserve by no means to be slighted, as he is the first that ever gave the public a tolerably complete edition of Chaucer; and

"*fuisse Græcos in vehementius negando per* DUO NEGA-
"TIVA; *tametsi Chaucerus (literarum Græcarum igna-*
"*rus) more sui temporis, in quo Saxonismus non penitus*
"*exoleverat,* DUOBUS NEGATIVIS *est usus**." He
next produces some instances in the Saxon, where not
only two, but three, and four negatives are put together with a negative signification.

It is not pretended, that all the obsolete words and
phrases, found in our author, are here collected, but
such alone as appear to have been immediately borrowed from Chaucer. Several antique expressions are
here unnoticed, which indeed are used by Chaucer,
but which are equally common to Lidgate, Gower,
and the author of *Piers Plowman's Visions.* Spenser
copied the language of most of the elder english poets,
but not without distinction. Chaucer was the source
from which he confessedly drew the largest draughts,
THE WELL OF ENGLISH UNDEFILED.

I cannot dismiss this Section without a wish, that
this neglected author, whom Spenser proposed as the

and though he is censured as one *antiqui nihil sapiens*, yet it must be allowed, that his Glossary to Chaucer, as being the first of that kind, was a very laudable undertaking; and though the first, that it is, notwithstanding, so well executed, as to have supplied very valuable materials to some more modern glossographers upon our antient bard.

* Linguarum Vet. Septentrional. *Thesaurus.* cap. 12, p. 58.

pattern

pattern of his ſtyle, and to whom he is indebted for many noble inventions, ſhould be more univerſally ſtudied. This is at leaſt what one might expect in an age of reſearch and curioſity. Chaucer is regarded rather as an old, than as a good, poet. We look upon his poems as venerable relics, not as beautiful compoſitions; as pieces better calculated to gratify the antiquarian than the critic. He abounds not only in ſtrokes of humour, which is commonly ſuppoſed to be his ſole talent, but of pathos, and ſublimity, not unworthy a more refined age. His old manners, his romantic arguments, his wildneſs of painting, his ſimplicity and antiquity of expreſſion, tranſport us into ſome fairy region, and are all highly pleaſing to the imagination. It is true that his uncouth and unfamiliar language diſguſts and deters many readers: but the principal reaſon of his being ſo little known, and ſo ſeldom taken into hand, is the convenient opportunity of reading him with pleaſure and facility in modern imitations. For when tranſlation, and ſuch imitations from Chaucer may be juſtly called, at length becomes ſubſtituted as the means of attaining a knowledge of any difficult and antient author, the original not only begins to be neglected and excluded as leſs eaſy, but alſo to be deſpiſed as leſs ornamental and elegant. Thus the public taſte becomes imperceptibly

tibly vitiated, while the genuine model is superseded, and gradually gives way to the establishment of a more specious, but false, resemblance. Thus, too many readers, happy to find the readiest accommodation for their indolence and their illiteracy, think themselves sufficient masters of Homer from Pope's translation: and thus, by an indiscreet comparison, Pope's translation is commonly preferred to the grecian text, in proportion as the former is furnished with more frequent and shining metaphors, more lively descriptions, and in general appears to be more full and florid, more elaborate and various.

SECT. VI.

Of Spenser's Imitations of Ariosto.

THE Circumstance of the Red-crosse knight and Una, meeting with Archimago disguised like a hermit, who entertains them with a fictitious tale, and afterwards raises two spirits, with intent to deceive the Red-crosse knight, seems to be copied from Ariosto. Angelica meets an hypocritical hermit, who raises a false spirit with a design to deceive Sacrapant and Renaldo, and to exasperate them against Orlando, &c. *Che*

Che scontro un' eremita, &c. *

But Spenser has greatly improved the hint. Archimago is again introduced after the same manner, B. 1. C. 6. s. 34. and B. 2. c. 1. s. 8.

B. i. c. ii.

This illusion effected by Archimago, who discovers a fictitious Una to the Red-crosse knight, engaged in the embraces of a young 'squire, seems to be imitated from the deceptions carried on in the enchanted castle of Atlanta, where many of the guests are imposed upon by false representations of the persons of their friends or mistresses; and more particularly, from that passage where Orlando, after having been deluded with the appearance of a counterfeit Angelica, is made to hear her cry out for his assistance, as if some ruffian was insulting and ravishing her, &c.

Dunque in presenzia del mio caro Orlando
Da questo ladro mi sarà rapita?
Piu, &c. &c †.

Helpe now or never helpe; alas! shall I,
In mine Orlando's sight loose my virginitie?
Harrington.

* C. 2. s. 12. † C. 12. s. 15.

B. i.

B. i. c. vii. f. xxxiii.

His warlike shield all closely cover'd was
Ne might of mortal eye be ever seene.
* * * * * * * * * *

xxxiv.

The fame to wight he never would disclose,
But when as monsters huge he would dismay,
Or daunt unequall armies, &c.
* * * * * * * * * *

xli.

And when he lift the prouder lookes subdew
He would them gazing blind, &c.

This is the shield of Atlanta.

D' un bello drappo di seta havea coperto
Lo SCUDO *in braccio il cavalier celeste,*
Come avesse, non so, tanto sofferto
Di tenerlo nascosto in quella veste;
Ch' immantinente, che lo mostra aperto,
Forza e chi 'l mira abbarbagliato reste,
E cada, come corpo morto cade *. —

This heavenly hellish warrior bare a shield
On his left arme, that had a silken case,
I cannot any cause or reason yeeld,
Why he should keep it coverd so long space:

* C. 2. f. 55.

It had such force that whoso it beheld,
Such shining light it striketh in their face,
That down they fell, &c. — — Harrington.

B. i. c. viii. f. iii.

— — — Wide wonders of all
Of that same hornes great vertues weren told.
* * * * * * * * *

iv.

Was never wight that heard that shrilling sound
But trembling feare did feele in every vaine.

This horn, with its miraculous effects, is borrowed from that which Logestylla presents to Astolfo.

*Dico, che 'l corno è di sì orribil suono,
Ch' ovunque s' ode, fa fuggir la gente.
Non puo, &c*.* — — —

An horne in which if he do once but blow
The noise thereof shall trouble men so sore,
That all both stout and faint shall flie therefro.
                                                    Harrington.

I wonder Spenser should have made so little use of this horn. He has not scrupled to introduce the shield

* C. 15. f. 15.

above-

above-mentioned, though as manifeftly borrowed fromAriofto, upon various occafions.

Turpin mentions a wonderful horn which belonged to Roland *. Olaus Magnus relates, that this horn which was called *Olivant,* was won, together with the fword *Durenda,* fo much celebrated in Ariofto, from the giant Jatmundus by Roland; that its miraculous effects were frequently fung by the old Iflandic bards in their fpirited odes, and that it might be heard at the diftance of twenty miles †. Thus, in conformity to the laft circumftance, in Don Quixote we are told, that in Ronfcevalles, where Charlemagne was defeated, Orlando's horn was to be feen as big as a great beam. The founding a horn was a common expedient for diffolving an enchantment. Cervantes alludes to this incident of romance, where the Devil's horn is founded as a prelude to the difenchanting of Dulcinea ‡. Boyardo and Berni have both their magical horns. Virgil's *Alecto's Horn* is as high and extravagant as any thing of the kind in romance.

— — — — — *Cornuque recurvo*
Tartaream intendit vocem, qua protenus omne

* Hift. Car. Mag. cap. 23.
† *De Aureo Cornu,* &c. Hafniæ. 1541. pag. 27, 29.
‡ B. 7. par. 2.

Contremuit

Contremuit nemus, et sylvæ intonuere profundæ.
Audiit et Triviæ longe lacus, audiit amnis
Sulphurea Nar albus aqua *.

A strong imagination is not commonly supposed to be one of Virgil's attributes. I think he greatly excels in painting the TERRIBLE.

It is remarkable, to recur to what is mentioned above, concerning the wonders of Orlando's horn being sung by the northern bards, that the old Islandic chroniclers have left us the atchievements of Charlemagne, and of king Arthur, among their histories, viz. " SAGAN AF KARLAMAGNUSE, &c. the history of Charlemagne, and of his champions and leaders. 1. Of his birth, coronation, &c. especially of the famous fight of Carvetus king of Babylon, with Oddegir the dane. 2. Of Aglandus king of Africa, and his son Jatmundus, and of their wars in Spain, with Charlemagne. 3. *Bruar thattur*, of Roland, &c. &c."
────── " SAGAN AF IVENT, &c. the history of Ivent, king Arthur's principal champion: containing, his battles with the giants, &c." ────── " HISTORICAL RHYMES of king Arthur; containing his league with Charlemagne." With many others of the same

* Æneid. l. 7. v. 513.

kind; particularly of the PUGILES *regis Arthuri*. These stories they partly new-moulded with names and facts from their own annals. Among the rest, they celebrated a king of England, not mentioned as I recollect, in our old histories, "SAGAN AF ALEFLECK, "the history of Alefleck, king of England, son of "Ridgare, and of his travels into Tartary, and India, "&c." We have also, in their TROJOMANNA SAGAN, the history of the siege of Troy, the voyage of Jason, &c. In their SAGAN AF GIBBON, they mention the giant *Askapart*, so well-known in our old romances*. This may seem to invalidate the doctrine delivered above †, That the fictions of chivalry prevailed in Europe, before the crusades. In another of their SAGAS, Jarl, a magician, descended from Odin, is introduced exhibiting his feats of necromancy before Charlemagne.

B. i. c. viii. s. xlvi.

Duessa, who just before appeared young and beautiful, divested of her rich apparel is discovered to be a lothsome old woman. She is a copy of Ariosto's Alcina, who having long engaged the affections of

* See Wanley's second vol. to Hickes's Thes. pag. 314. seq. These are all antient Scandic manuscripts at Stockholm.

† Pag. 64.

Rogero,

Rogero, by the counterfeited charms of youth and beauty, is at laſt, by the virtue of his ring, found to be old and ugly. Theſe circumſtances of Dueſſa's diſcovery, are literally tranſlated from the italian poet.

    A loathly wrinkled hag, ill-favour'd, old;
    * * * * * * * * *
               xlvii.
    Her crafty head was altogether bald,
    And, — — —
    Was overgrowne with ſcurfe, and filthy ſcalde,
    Her teeth out of her rotten gums were feld.

    Pallido, creſpo, e macilenta avea
    Alcina il viſo, il crin raro, e canuto,
    * * * * * * * * *
    Ogni dente di bocca era caduto *.

    Her face was wan, a leane and withheld ſkin,
    * * * * * * * * *
    Her haire was gray of hue, and verie thin,
    Her teeth were gone, &c. —— Harrington.

        B. ii. c. iv. ſ. xix.

    It was my fortune, &c. — — —

This tale is borrowed from the tale of Geneura in Orlando Furioſo, c. 4. ſ. 50.

       * C. 7. ſ. 73.

B. ii. c. xi. f. xxxvii.

The difficulty which prince Arthur finds in killing Maleger, seems to be copied from the encounter of Griffin and Aquilant with Orillo, who, like Maleger, receives no injury from all the wounds that are given him: and the circumstances by which Maleger's death is effected, partake much of the fantastic extravagance of those by which Orillo is at last killed. See Orland. Fur. c. 15. f. 67. &c. &c.

B. iii. c. iv. f. lix.

— — — — A mighty speare,
Which Bladud made by magicke art of yore.
* * * * * * * * *
For never wight so fast in sell could sit,
But him perforce unto the ground it bore.

This *enchanted* spear of Britomartis is the LANCE *d'oro*, which Astolfo presents to Bradamante.

La lancia, che di quanti ne percuote
Fà le selle restar subito vote *.

The speare, — — —
With head thereof if any touched were,
Straight ways to fall to ground they must be fayne.
Harrington.

* C. 23. f. 15.
Spenser

Spenser sometimes calls it *Goldelaunce.*

B. iii. c. iv. f. i.

> Where is the antique glory now become,
> That whilome wont in women to appeare?
> Where be the brave atchievements done by some?

This introduction in praise of women, seems to be enlarged from that of Ariosto, to c. 20.

> *La donne antiche hanno mirabil cose,*
> *Fatto ne l' arme, e ne le sacre muse,*
> *E di lor opre belle, e gloriose*
> *Gran lume in tutto il mondo si diffuse.*
> *Arpalice, e Camilla son famose,*
> *Perche in battaglia erano esperte, &c.*

> Marvellous deeds by divers dames were donne
> In times of old, as well by sword as pen;
> So as their glory shined like the sunne,
> And famous was both far and neare, as then
> The fame Harpalice in battel won,
> Camilla's worth, &c. — —   Harrington.

And, b. 3, c. 2. f. 1. he touches upon the same argument again.

> Here have I cause in men just blame to find
> That in their proper praise too partiall bee,

And

And not indifferent to woman-kind,
To whom no fhare in armes and chivalrie
They do impart, ne maken memorie
Of their brave gefts, and proweffe martiall;
Scarce do they fpare to one, or two, or three,
Roome in their writs; yet the fame writing fmall
Does all their deeds deface, and dims their glories all.

Where he feems to copy the clofe of the above introduction of Ariofto.

E forfe afcofi han lor debiti onori
L' invidia; e il non faper degli fcrittori*.

Doubtleffe the fault is either in back-biters,
Or want of fkill, and judgment in the writers.

Harrington.

B. iii. c. iii. f. xx.

Merlin here difcovers to Britomart her future progeny; which he does likewife to Bradamante in Ariofto, c. 3.

B. iii. c. vii. f. lii.

But read thou fquire of dames, &c. ———

The tale of the Squire of Dames, is a copy of the Hoft's tale, in Ariofto. c. 28.

* S. 2.

B. iii. c. x. f. xlvii.

Malbecco mixes with the flock of goats, and paffes for one. He might have here the efcape of Ulyffes from Polypheme in his eye; but more immediately, perhaps, the like expedient made ufe of by Norandin, who mixes among the goats, as a goat, that he may gain accefs to Lucina. c. 17. f. 35. &c. Norandin, indeed, is dreffed up in goat-fkins, but Malbecco's fimilitude is made out by his horns, which he wears as a cuckold; a fiction, the meannefs of which nothing but the beautiful transformation, at the end of the Canto, could have made amends for.

B. iv. c. i. xiii.

With that her gliftring helmet fhe unlaced,
Which doft, her golden locks that were upbound,
Still in a knott unto her heeles downe traced.

Marfifa thus difcovers herfelf,

Al trar degli elmi tutti vider come
Havea lor dato ajuto una donzella.
Fa conofciuta a l'auree crefpe chiome
Ed a la faccia delicata, &c *

* C. 26. f. 28.

Now when Marfifa had put off her bever,
To be a woman everie one perceive her.

XXV.

Her golden hair truft up with carelefs grace,
Her forehead faire, &c. — —   Harrington.

A few ftanzas before fhe is compared to Bellona,

Stimato egli hauria lei forfe Bellona.   ft. 24.

So our author, ft. 14.

Some, that Bellona in that warlike guife
To them appear'd. — — — —

See a like Difcovery. 3. 9. 20. 21.

Spenfer's Britomart is a manifeft copy of Ariofto's Bradamante and Marfifa.

B. iv. c. ii. f. iv.

——— The bold Sir FERRAUGH hight.

Sir *Ferragh* is one of Ariofto's knights. But it is not at the fame time improbable, that Spenfer might adopt this name in Ireland; this poem being written during his refidence there. He informs us, in his *State of Ireland,* that, " The Irifh, in all their in-
" counters, ufe a very common word, crying FER-
" RAGH, FERRAGH; which is a fcottifh word, to
" wit,

" wit, the name of one of the firſt kings of Scotland,
" called FERAGUS, or FERGUS." And afterwards
he ſays, " There be yet, at this day, in Ireland, many
" iriſhmen..... called by the name of FERRAGH."

B. iv. c. iii. ſ. xlv.

Much more of price, and of more gracious powre
Is this, then that ſame water of Ardenne;
The which Renaldo drunke in happy houre,
Deſcribed by that famous Tuſcane penne;
For that had might to change the harts of men
From love to hate. — — — —

That famous Tuſcan penne, ARIOSTO, deſcribes two fountains in Ardenna, from one of which Renaldo drinks, and from the other Angelica.

E queſto hanno cauſato due fontane,
Che di diverſo effetto hanno liquore;
Ambe in Ardenna, e non ſono lontane.
D' amoroſo diſio l' una empie il core,
Chi bee dell' altra, ſenza amor rimane,
E volge tutto in ghiaccio il primo ardore.
Renaldo guſtò d' una, e amor lo ſtrugge;
Angelica de l' altra, e l'odia, e fugge*.

* C. 1. ſ. 78.

The caufe of this firft from two fountains grew,
Like in the tafte, but in th' effects unlike,
Plafte in Ardenna, ech in others vew,
Who taftes the one love's dart his heart doth ftrike;
Contrarie of the other doth enfew,
Who drinke thereof their lovers fhall miflike;
Renaldo dranke of one, and love much pained him,
The other dranke this damfell, and difdained him.

         Harrington.

From Spenfer's account of this WATER of ARDENNE it might he concluded, that Rinaldo drank of the fountain which turned love into hate; but it appears from this paffage inAriofto, that he drank of the fountain which produced the contrary effect. However, it is manifeft, that our author alludes to another ftanza inAriofto, where Renaldo drinks of that fountain which produced the effect here defcribed by Spenfer. c. 42. f. 63.

    B. v. c. ii. f. iv.

———— ———— ———— ———— Here beyond,
A curfed cruell Sarazin doth wonne,
That keepes a bridges paffage by ftrong hand;
And many errant knights hath there foredonne.

Thus the pagan in Ariofto, 29. 35. keeps a bridge, which no man can pafs over unlefs he fights with him;
              and

and which occasions many combats in the water, one of which sort is here described between Sir Arthegall and the Saracen. f. 11.

In MORTE ARTHUR we find an account of a knight who kept a bridge, in which a circumstance is mentioned, not in Ariosto, which Spenser seems to have copied from thence, in the passage under consideration. " On the third day he rode over a long
" bridge; and there start upon him sodainly a pas-
" sing fowle chorle, and he smote his horse, and
" asked him, why he rode over that bridge with-
" out his licence *."

So Spenser,

> Who as they to the passage gan to draw,
> A villaine came to them with scull all raw,
> That passage-money did of them require. st. 11.

B. v. c. iii. f. xxxiv.

And called Brigadore. — — —

BRIGADORE is the name of the knights horse. BRIGLIADORO also is the name of Orlando's horse; from *Briglia d'oro*, a golden bridle.

* B. 1, c. III.

On

On the affectation, so common in books of chivalry, of dignifying horses, as well as knights, with pompous names, the following ridicule in Cervantes is founded. " And pray, said Sancho, how many persons will this horse carry? Two, replied the Afflicted; one upon the saddle, and the other upon the crupper, and these are commonly the knight and the squire, when there is no damsel to be stolen. I should be glad to know, Afflicted Madam, what is the name of that same horse? His name, answered the Afflicted, is not like that of Bellerophon's horse, which was called *Pegasus*, nor does it resemble that which distinguished the horse of Alexander the Great, *Bucephalus*; nor that of Orlando Furioso, whose name was *Brilliadoro*; nor *Bayarte*, which belonged to Reynaldo de Montalvan; nor *Frontino*, that appertained to Rugero; nor *Bootes*, nor *Peritoa*, the horses of the Sun; nor is he called *Orelia*, like that steed upon which the unfortunate Rodrigo, last king of the Goths, engaged in that battle where he lost his crown and life. I will lay a wager, cried Sancho, that as he is not distinguished by any of those famous names of horses, so well known, so neither have they given him the name of my master's horse *Rozinante*, &c *." After the same manner, they

---

* Don Quixote, b. 3. ch. 8.

named

named their swords. Thus *Chrysaor* is the name of Arthegal's sword; 5. 1. 9. *Caliburn* of king Arthur's, in *Morte Arthur*, &c. Thus too in Ariosto, we have Renaldo's *Fusberta*, Rogero's *Balisarda*, and Orlando's *Durindana*. *Durinda* is the name of Roland's sword in Turpin's Romance, which Ariosto and Boyardo copy so faithfully. As a specimen of that historian's style and manner, I shall present the reader with Roland's soliloquy addressed to this sword, when he was mortally wounded by a saracen giant. " *O ensis pulcherrime, sed semper lucidissime, capulo* " *eburneo candidissime, cruce aurea splendissime, superfi-* " *cie deaurate, pomo beryllino deaurate, magno nomine* " *dei insculpte, acumine legitime, virtute omni prædite,* " *quis amplius virtute tua utetur? Quis, &c* *." Arthur's sword is called *Mordure* by Spenser; and his shield, or banner, *Pridwen*, and his spear *Roan*, by the romance-writers. *Morglay* was the sword of sir Bevys of Southampton, and *Galantine* of sir Gawaine. *Tizona* was the name they gave the sword of Roderick Diaz de Bivar, the famous spanish general against the Moors. The french always applied the epithet *joyeuse*, jocose, to the sword of their grand hero Charlemagne. This, as one of their own countrymen observes, is a

---

* I. Turpini Hist. de Gestis Caroli Mag. cap. 22.

strong

strong characteristic of their natural gaiety; which a phlegmatic englishman would call ridiculous levity.
" *Ils ont continuellement repandu sur toutes les images de la guerre un air d'enjouement, qui leur est propre: ils n'ont jamais parle que comme d'une fete, d'un jeu, et d'un passe-temps.* Jouer leur jeu, *ont-ils dit les arbaletriers qui faisoient pleuvoir une grele de traits:* Jouer gros jeu, *pour donner battaille:* Jouer des mains; *et une infinité d'autres façons de parler semblables se recontrent souvent dans la lecture de recits militaires de nos ecrivains. Froissart, en rapportant la mort de duc Winceslas, fait ainsi son portrait;* En celuy temps [1383] trespassa de ce siecle .... le gentil et *joly* duc Winceslas de Boheme, duc de Luxemburgh et de Brabant, qui en son temps, noble, *frisque, sage, amoreux, et armeret* avoit este *."
Some of their late campaigns have begun in the same spirit; which, however, have often ended very seriously: nor have the *balls* and the *battles* of those lively generals, Soubise and Broglio, been always executed with equal good humour and brilliancy.

B. v. c. ix. f. xi.

He is describing *Guile.*

Als at his back a great wide net he bore,

---

* M. de la Curne de S. Palaye. supr. citat. tom. ii. pag. 65. Not.

With

With which he seldom fished at the brooke,
But us'd to fish for fooles on the dry shore.

This net seems to be borrowed from the like expedient used by the giant Caligorante.

Piacer fra tanta crudelta si prende
D'una Rete, &c *.

And in this crueltie he has great sport
To use the service of a certaine net.   Harrington.

B. vi. c. xi. s. ii.

Like as is now befalne to this faire maid,
Faire Pastorell, &c. — — — —

The distress of Pastorell is somewhat similar to that of Ariosto's Isabel, who is seized by certain outlaws or pirates, and imprisoned in a cave, in order to be sold for a slave †.

This pastoral part of the FAIRY QUEEN seems to have been occasioned by Sydney's *Arcadia*, and in conformity to the common fashion of the times, which abounded in pastoral poetry.

Hence our author.

* C. 15. s. 44. seq.   † C. 12. s. 91. seq.

> Our pleafant groves which planted were with paines,
> That with our muficke wont fo oft to ring,
> And arbors fweet in which the fhepherd fwaines
> Were *wont fo oft their* PASTORALS *to fing,*
> They have cut downe, and all their pleafance mard,
> That now *no paftoral* is to be hard *.

And Hall, in the Prologue * to his Satires, publifhed in 1597.

> Would yee but breathe within a wax-bound quill,
> Pan's feven-fold pipe, fome *plaintive* PASTORAL;
> To teach each hallow'd grove, and fhrubbie hill,
> Each murmuring brook, and folitarie vale,
> To found our love, and to our fong accord,
> Wearying echo with one changeleffe word †.

And in the firft Satire, he declares that he cannot follow the fafhionable cant of the times.

> Nor under everie bank, and everie tree,
> Speake rimes unto mine oaten minftralfie ‡.

The Mifcellanies of queen Elizabeth's age, and of the following reign, are filled with this fpecies of poetry, in which it was ufual for every young writer, at leaft, to try his fkill. The firft collection of paftorals

---

* Tears of the Mufes.   † *A Defiance to Envie,* b. 1. f. 14.
‡ B. 1. f. 1.

I have

(219)

I have met with in englifh, is, I think, in " *Eglogs,* " *Epitaphs, and Sonnets, newly written by Barnabie* " *Googe, &c.* 1563." Googe was the tranflator of Palingenius. The ftudy of the italian poets, particularly the recent publication of the *Profa* of Sannazarius, which certainly gave rife to the *Arcadia,* produced this inundation of paftorals. Taffo's *Aminta* was now too but juft publifhed, and came extremely popular. Thefe Spenfer copied; but one of his moft finifhed and elegant paftorals, *December,* is literally tranflated from old Clement Marot, which is not obferved by the commentator, E. K. I will give great part of the french at length, which, as alfo the remainder, the reader may compare with the englifh at his leifure.

Un Paftoreau, qui Robin s' appelloit,
* * * * * * * * *
Parmi faufteaux, arbres qui font ombrage,
* * * * * * * *
Chantant ainfi: O Pan, dieu fouverain,
Qui de garder ne fus onc pareffeux
Parcs, et brebis, et les maiftres d'iceux,
Et remets fur tous gentils paftoureaux,
Quand ils n' ont prez, ne loges, ne toreaux,
Je te fupply (fi onc en ces bas eftres
Daignas ouyr chanfonnettes champeftres)

F f 2 *Efcoute*

Escoute un peu, de ton verd cabinet
Le chant rural de petit Robinet.

Sur le printemps de ma jeuneſſe folle,
Je reſemblois l'arondelle, qui volle
Puis ça, puis la : l'aage me conduiſoit
Sans peur, ne ſoing, ou le cœur me diſoit.
En la foreſt (ſans la crainte des loups)
Je m'en allois ſouvent cueilir le houx,
Pour faire gluz a prendre oyſeaux ramages,
Tous differens de chant, et de plumages :
On me ſoulois (pour le prendre) entremettre
A faire brics, ou cages pour les mettre :
Ou tranſnovoys les rivieres profondes,
Ou r'enforcois ſur le genoil le frondes,
Puis d'en tirer, droit, et loing j'apprenois,
Pour chaſſer loups, abattre des noix.

O quantefois aux arbres grimpe j'ay
Pour deſnicher ou la pie, ou le geay;
Ou pour jetter des fruits ja meurs, et beaux,
A mes compaignes, qui tendoient leurs chapeaux.
Aucunesfois aux montaignes alloye,
Aucunesfois aux foſſes, &c.
* * * * * * * * * *
Deſia pourtant je faiſois quelques nottes

De

(221)

De chant rustique, et dessoubz les ormeaux
Quasi enfant sonnois de chalumeaux.
Si ne saurois bien dire, ne penser,
Qui m' enseigna sitost d'y commencer
Ou la nature aux muses inclinee
Ou ma fortune, en cela destinee
A te servir : si ce ne fut l'un d'eux,
Je suis certain, que ce furent tous d'eux.

  Ce que voyant le bon Janot, mon pere,
Voulut gager a Jaquet son compere,
Contre un veau gras, deux Aignelets bessons,
Que quelque jour je serois des chansons
A ta louenge, O Pan dieu tressacrè,
Voire chansons qui te viendroient a grè.

* * * * * * * *

Il me souloit, une leçon donner
Pour doucement la musette entonner.

* * * * * * * *

  Quand printemps fault, et l' esté comparoist, &c*.

It has been before observed, that Spenser took his BLATANT beast, from the QUESTING beast in *Morte Arthur*. But yet I am of opinion, that in representing Scandal under the shape of a monstrous and un-

---

* EGLOGUE au roy souz le noms de *Pan* et *Robin*. Les Oeuvres, ed. a Paris, 1551. pag. 19. 12mo.

natural

natural beaft, at the fame time he copied Ariofto, who has figured Avarice and Jealoufy under the picture of two hideous monfters; the firft of which, like Spenfer's BLATANT *beaft*, attacks all conditions of life alike; enters the palace as well as the cottage, but vents his rage in a more particular manner againft the clergy, fparing not even the pope himfelf. She is fuppofed at laft to be bound by Leo X. while Jealoufy is driven to her den by Renaldo. Luther and Calvin have fuffered the fame fignificant transformations from the hands of the painters; and are often exhibited, in the churches abroad, under the forms of terrible dragons, and other deteftable figures, expiring beneath the feet of triumphant popery. It feems probable, that thefe allegorical beafts, formed of the moft frightful combinations, firft took their rife from the beaft in the *Revelations*, which " rofe out of the fea, " having feven heads, and ten horns, and upon his " horns ten crowns, and upon his heads the name of " *blafphemy*; and the beaft which I faw was like unto " a leopard, and his feet were as the feet of a bear, " and his mouth as the mouth of a lion [*]."

The reader will excufe my adding, in this place, a beautiful paffage which Spenfer has drawn from

---

[*] Revel. c. 13. v. 1. 2. feq. See Fairy Queen. 8. 12. 23. and Orl. Fur. c. 26. f. 27. and c. 62. f. 44.

his favorite italian poet, in the *Mourning Muse of Thestylis*.

> The blinded archer-boy,
>   Like larke in showre of raine,
> Sate bathing of his wings,
>   And glad the time did spend
> Under those cryftall drops,
>   Which fall from her faire eyes,
> And at their brighteft beames,
>   Him proynd in lovely wife.

Cosi a la belle lagrime le piume
Se bagna Amore, e gode al chiaro lume*.

So the blind god, whose force no man can shunne,
Sits in her eyes, and thence his darts doth fling;
Bathing his wings in her cleare cryftal ftreames,
And funning them in her rare beauties beames.
Harrington.

Though it muft be confeffed, that Spenfer's verfes bear a ftronger refemblance to thefe of Nic. Archias, of a lady weeping.

Tam suavi in pluvia nitens Cupido
Insidebat, uti solet volucris
Ramo, vere novo, ad novos tepores

* C. 11. f. 65.

Post

Post solem accipere ætheris liquores,
Gestire et pluviæ ore blandiendo *.

I shall add, that Spenser, in his Radegond, with her city of females, had an eye upon Ariosto's land of Amazons. It is however to be remembered, that a land of Amazons is a frequent miracle of romance, being taken from the old legends of the Trojan war. Caxton, in his *Destruction of Troy*, gives us a chapter, " How the queene Panthasile cam from *Amazonne*, " with a thousand maydens, to the socoure of Troye. " And how she bare her valyantly, &c †."

But although Spenser studied Ariosto with such attention, insomuch that he was ambitious of rivalling the *Orlando Furioso* in a poem formed on a similar plan, yet the genius of each was entirely different. Spenser, amidst all his absurdities, abounds with beautiful and

* See the works of Fracastorius, pag. 238. *Patavii*, 1718. 8vo.

† See Caxton's *Recuyel of the Historys of Troye*. This book was translated from the french of Raoul le Feure, Chaplain to the duke of Burgundy, who compiled it A. D. 1464, from divers latin books on the the same subject. The translation was finished, A. D. 1471. It was the first piece printed by Caxton. Lidgate had written, many years before, *The Historie, Siege, and Destruction of Troye*, at the *Commandement of Kynge Henrie* V. 1412, in english verse. Guido de Columpnys, mentioned in Chaucer's *House of Fame*, [3. 381.] was, among others, a favorite author on this subject. He was of Messina in Sicily, and wrote the history of Troy in latin, after Dictys Cretensis, 1278. Chaucer also places Dares Phrygius in his House of Fame, [ib. 379.] among the famous writers, poets, and historians, who were " *busie for to bere up Troye.*"

sublime

sublime representations; while Ariosto's strokes of true poetry bear no proportion to his sallies of merely romantic imagination. He gives us the grotesque for the graceful, and extravagance for majesty. He frequently moves our laughter by the whimsical figures of a Callot, but seldom awakens our admiration by the just portraits of a Raphael. Ariosto's vein is essentially different from Spenser's; it is absolutely comic*, and infinitely better suited to scenes of humour, than to serious and solemn description. He so characteristically excels in painting the familiar manners, that those detached pieces in the *Orlando* called Tales, are by far the most shining passages in the poem. Many of his similes are also glaring indications of his predominant inclination to ridicule†.

* I cannot forbear subjoining an anecdote, which highly displays Ariosto's early and strong disposition to drollery and humour. His father one day severely chiding him, Ariosto heard him with great attention, without urging a syllable in excuse of his fault. His brother, as soon as the father was departed, asked him, why he had made no defence or reply. Ariosto answered, that he was just at that instant writing a comedy, and that he was got to a scene, in which was introduced an old man chiding his son; and that the moment his father opened his mouth it came into his head, to examine him with attention, that he might paint after nature: that he was therefore entirely engrossed in watching the gestures, tone, and expressions of his father; and never had the least thought of making him any apology. Hist. de Theat. Ital. par Riccoboni. p. 145. Lond. 1728.

* Thus the magician disclosing his enchanted shield, to dazzle the sight of Bradamante, is compared to a cat wantonly playing with a mouse,

But if there should be any readers, who, from some of the fictions in Orlando, would prove that its author possessed an extensive and elevated invention, let them remember, that these are commonly borrowed from romances, and applied by the poet to the tenor of his allegory. Yet even here, he gives no proofs of a strong imagination. For although romances were his ground-work, yet it appears, that he was more fond of imitating their enormous improbabilities, than of adorning his poetry with the more glorious and genuine colourings of their magnificent conceptions.

Ariosto's mixture of burlesque and serious is thus defended by Gravina. " Ariosto could not have attained his end, nor could his readers have reaped that instruction which poetry aims at, if this poem had not

mouse, and at last killing it. c. 4. f. 22. Rogero fighting with the orc, a sea monster, is compared to a fly attacking a mastiff, and atempting to sting him in various parts of his body. c. 10. f. 105. Aldirdo being slain by Orlando, his soldiers are said to make a noise like a erd of swine, when a wolf has seized one of their little pigs, *un tener porco*. c. 12. f. 78. Zerbino having first insulted Gabrina, and afterwards addressing her in a gentle manner, is compared to a dog, who at first furiously assaults a stranger, but afterwards, a crust being thrown, fawns upon him. c. 20. f. 139. Orlando and Mandricard fighting together, their weapons being broke to pieces, are compared to two peasants who are drubbing each other, having quarrelled about a watercourse, or boundary of land. c. 23. f. 83. Other examples of this sort are obvious to a reader of Ariosto. These comparisons may be said to be of the Homeric kind; but, I fear, what was simplicity in Homer, is burlesque in Ariosto.

described

described not only great actions in general, but, in some places, those that are mean and low. So that by this conduct, every passion, and every species of behaviour, was imitated. Whence, the reader might perceive what he should avoid or embrace in the common practice of civil life, according to the beauty or deformity of each object so described. This mixture of various persons, introduced with art, not only resembles the productions of nature, which are never simple, but always compounded, but is by no means unsuitable to the common course of heroic actions, which are still carried on by the co-operations of inferior instruments and agents. . . . . . Wherefore, after the example of Homer, Ariosto did not imagine that sublimity excluded a moderate and necessary use of mean personages. To such a variety of persons and things, it was requisite also to adapt a variety of stile *."

Voltaire observes truly; " Les Grecs et les Latins
" employerent d'abord la poesie à peindre les objects
" sensibles de toute la nature. Homere exprime tout
" ce qui frape les yeux : les François, qui n'ont
" guere commence à perfectionner la grande poesie
" qu'au un Theatre, n'ont pû et n'ont dû exprimer

* Della Ragion Poetica. ed. Naples, 1716. lib. 2. c. 16. pag. 205.

" alors

" alors que ce qui peut toucher l'ame. Nous nous
" fommes interdits nous-memes infenfiblement prefque
" tous les objects que d'autres nations ont osè prendre.
" Il n'eft rien que le Dante n'exprimât, A L'EX-
" AMPLE DES ANCIENS: IL ACCOUTUMA LES
" ITALIENS A TOUT DIRE. Mais nous, comment
" pourions-nous adjourdhui imiter l'auteur des Geor-
" giques, qui nomme fans detour tous les inftruments
" de l'agriculture? *"

After all, may we not afk, Does not the nature of heroic poetry confift in a due SELECTION of objects? Are not importance and dignity its effential properties? Is it not its immediate province to feparate high from low, fair from deformed; to compound rather than to copy nature, and to prefent thofe exalted combinations, which never exifted together, amid the general and neceffary defects of real life?

* Difc. de M. Voltaire, a l'academie François. OEUVRES, p. 181. tom. 5. 1756. 8vo. See Boileau's Differtation fur la Joconde. OEU-VRES. Paris, 1747. p. 86. tom. 3. 8vo.

END OF THE FIRST VOLUME.

INDEX.

A.

ABBE DU BOS, *his censure of Ariosto's Orlando Furioso*, I. 14. *Condemns those painters who introduce their own allegories into sacred subjects*, II. 97.
Academicians, della Crusca, *prefer Ariosto to Tasso*, I. 3.
Action, allegorical, *why faulty*, II. 113.
ADONIS, *his gardens, Spenser founds his fiction concerning them on ancient mythology*, I. 89.
𝔄𝔡𝔬𝔯𝔢 and 𝔄𝔡𝔬𝔯𝔫, II. 201.
AGAVE, *her story*, I. 101.
AGDISTES, a GENIUS, I. 82.
Alexandrine verses, *rules concerning them*, II. 154.
Allegories, *Spenser's manner of forming them accounted for*, II. 89. *Publickly shewn in Queen Elizabeth's time*, 90. *Capital faults in Spenser's*, 95. *Some of them examined*, 95, 98. *Spenser's manner of allegorising different from Ariosto's, and why*, 91.
Alliteration, *practised by the Saxon poets*, II. 215.
Amber-grease, *a seasoning in cookery*, I. 121.
Ambiguous expression, instances of, *in Spenser*, II. 34. *In Milton*, 35.
Anachronism, instances of, *in Spenser*, II. 21.
Antients, *imitate every thing*, I. 228.
ANTONINUS Liberalis, *a valuable compiler*, I. 94.
APOLLONIUS, Rhodius, *illustrated*, I. 105. *Copied by Milton*, 105, 111. *Illustrated*, II. 151.
ARCHIMAGO, instance of, *his hypocrisy, copied from Ariosto*, I. 198. *Of his illusion*, 199.
Architecture, antient, in England, *its gradations*, II. 184.
ARIOSTO, *imitates Boyardo*, I. 2. *Account of the plan of his poem*, 12. *His genius comic*, I. 225. *Defended*, 226.
Ardenne, water of, *Ariosto's mention of it alluded to by Spenser*, I. 211.

VOL. I. * 2

(vi)

Arte of English poesie, author of, *condemns Spenser's obsolete stile in his Pastorals*, I. 118. *Commends his Pastorals*, 122. *His account of singing to the harp in Queen Elizabeth's time*, 52. *Censures Skelton*, 52.

ARTHUR, Prince, *cannot properly be called the hero of the* FAERIE QUEENE, I. 6.

ARTHUR, King, *his round table*, I. 43, 65. 186. *Popularity of his story*, 41.

ASTRÆUS, a sea-god, *account of him*, I. 102.

Astronomy, *a favourite science in the dark ages*, II. 240.

AVARICE, Ariosto's, *why so represented*, I. 222.

B.

Bards, *introduced with propriety by Spenser*, II. 164.

Bale, II. 122.

Band, II. 161.

BEAUMONT and FLETCHER, *illustrated*, I. 41. II. 94. *Explained*, 201.

BELLONA, *Spenser misrepresents her birth*, I. 112.

BENI, *compares Ariosto with Homer*, I. 1.

BEVIS, Sir, of Southampton, *imitated by Spenser*, I. 46.

Bite, I. 168.

BLANDAMOUR, a name, *drawn from Chaucer, or from a romance so called*, I. 189.

BLATANT BEAST, *the hint of it taken from* Morte Arthur, *a romance*, I. 22. *Partly occasioned by Ariosto's description of Jealousy and Avarice*, 222.

Blood-guiltinesse, and Blood-thirstie, II. 139.

Brain-pan, II. 225.

BRAND, II. 259.

BRITAINE'S IDA, *not written by Spenser*, I. 123. *Criticism and conjectures concerning it*, 124.

Bridge, remarkable one, *copied from Ariosto, or from* Morte Arthur, I. 213.

BRIGADORE, name of a horse, *drawn from Ariosto*, I. 213.

BRITOMART, *how properly stiled the patroness of chastity*,

I. 84. *Her history*, 85. *Her discovery copied from Ariosto*, 209. *She is a copy of Ariosto's Marfisa, and Bradamante,* 209.

BUSYRANE, *whence drawn,* II. 173.

By Hooke or by Crooke, II. 205.

C.

CERVANTES, *illustrated,* I. 24, 65, 186, 202, 214. II. 34. 89. 124. 225.

Chambers, *how formerly adorned,* II. 222. 232.

Character'd, II. 162.

CHARLEMAGNE, *supposed to be the archetype of king Arthur,* I. 186. *Caxton's history of him,* II. 43. *Celebrated by the Islandic bards,* I. 203. *His sword,* 215.

CHARLES II. *the taste for poetry in his age, censured,* II. 111.

CHAUCER, *his stile copied by Spenser,* I. 124, 196. *And many of his sentiments,* 135. *Encomium upon him,* 125. *Corrected,* II. 62. *Why stiled one of the first english poets,* 103. *Explained,* I. 44. II. 160, 132.

Ceiris, *of Virgil, where copied by Spenser,* II. 254.

CERBERUS, *suppos'ed to be the proper reading in Milton's second verse of l' Allegro, and why,* I. 73.

Charm, II. 239.

Checklaton, I. 194.

Childed, II. 229.

CHIRON, *beautiful description of his astonishment, after hearing the music of Orpheus,* I. 111.

Chivalry, *practised in Queen Elizabeth's age,* I. 18. II. 90. *It's use and importance,* II. 226. *Books of, ridiculed by Chaucer,* I. 143. *Vindicated and recommended,* II. 267.

Clang, II. 143.

Croniclers, ISLANDIC, *specimen of their stories,* I. 203.

COCYTUS, *Spenser misrepresents mythology concerning it,* I. 80.

Commentators, *their difference of opinion accounted for,* II. 71.

(viii)

Concealment, *a source of the sublime*, II. 221.
Construction, confused, instances of, *in Spenser*, II. 13.
Contented and Concent, II. 166.
Conteck, I. 173.
CROMWELL, Oliver, *anecdote concerning*, II. 236.
CRUDOR, *his insolence and cruelty, copied from* Morte Arthur, I. 24.
CUPID and PSYCHE, *Spenser misrepresents Apuleius's account of them*, I. 90.
CUPID, *A representation of him copied from Chaucer*, I. 160. *A false one*, 161. *How represented by Catullus and Sappho*, 161. *A description of him copied from Ariosto, or from N. Archias*, 223.
Curtesie, *it's importance, in the character of a knight*, II. 20.

D.

Dance of Death, *account of prints so called*, II. 117. *Alluded to by Spenser*, 121.
DANGER, *personified from Chaucer*, I. 188.
Darraine, I. 164.
Death's Door, II. 181.
Despair, *why Spenser excelled in painting it*, II. 55.
Disple, II. 136.
Doen to Die, II. 168.
Douzepere, I. 184.
Dragon-encounters, *copied by Spenser from romance*, I. 54.
DRAYTON, *a romantic story borrowed by him from Geoffrey of Monmouth*, I. 26. *Where buried*, 25.
DRYDEN, *censured for affirming that prince Arthur appears in every part of the* FAERIE QUEENE, I. 7. *And for his manner of praising the Paradise Lost*, II. 112. *And for misrepresenting Milton's reason for chusing blank verse*, 112. *Imitates Spenser*, 140.
Dryghte, II. 217.
Duessa, *her discovery, copied from Ariosto*, I. 204.

(ix)

E.

EDWARD, Black Prince, *MS. metrical history of,* I. 1. 2.

E. K. the commentator on Spenser's Æglogues, *his reason why Spenser chose to write in an obsolete stile,* I. 126. *His real name,* 26.

Elfe, I. 55.

Elfes and Goblins, *whence derived,* I. 57.

Elficleos, king *Henry* vii. I. 57.

ELISABETH, queen, *flattered by Spenser,* II. 49. *Anecdote concerning,* 179. *Her maids of honour how employed,* 129.

Elleipsis, instances of, *in Spenser,* I. 4. *In Milton,* 12.

Embowd, II. 134.

Enchanted cup, story of, *from* Morte Arthur, I. 39.

English Language, *its corruptions about Queen Elizabeth's age,* I. 127. *Spenser's disapprobation of these corruptions, proved from his own words,* 130. *Notwithstanding he himself contributed to add to these corruptions, and why,* 132.

Endlong, I. 184.

ENVY, *Spenser's indelicacy in describing her,* I. 69. *And excellence,* 70.

F.

Faeries, *sometimes used for any ideal people,* I. 61. *Whence the fiction of them was derived,* 62. *Not always diminutive beings,* 63.

FAERIE Nation, *Spenser's original and genealogy of it explained,* I. 56.

FAERIE QUEENE, *a popular tradition,* I. 58. *Supposed to exist in King Arthur's time,* 58. *Spenser's poem so called, occasioned many imitations, on its publication, in which fairies were actors,* 59.

Falconry, History *of,* II. 171. Knowledge *of, an accomplishment in the character of a knight,* 171.

(x)

Fatall, II. 65.
Fear, *Spenser excels in painting it*, II. 53.
Ferraugh, Sir, *a name drawn from Ariosto*, I. 210.
File, I. 163.
Filed, II. 158.
Fleece, golden, expedition of, *a favourite story in romance*, I. 176. *Its romantic turn*, 178.
Florimel, false, *simile concerning her examined*, II. 206. *Story of her girdle whence taken*, I. 54.
Fountains, II. 151.
French, Poets, *more fond of familiar manners than sublime fiction*, II. 111.
Furies, *the antients afraid to name them*, I. 67.

G.

Galy Half-pence, *explained*, I. 180.
Gascoigne, George, *account of*, II. 167.
Gelli, his Circe, *afforded a hint to Spenser*, II. 153.
Geneura, tale of, in Ariosto, *copied by Spenser*, I. 205.
Genius, *a particular one, drawn by Spenser from N. Comes*, I. 82. *And a circumstance concerning him from Horace*, 83. *Another drawn from the picture of Cebes*, 83.
Giambeux, I. 194.
Glitterand, I. 167.
Glocester, Robert of, II. 102.
Gloriana, *the attainment of her the end of the* Faerie Queene. I. 6. *Prince Arthur improperly conducted to this end*, 6, 7.
Glode, I. 190. *Beautifully applied by Gower*, 191.
Goodfellow, Robin, I. 120.
Gorlois, story of, *alluded to by Milton*, II. 163.
Gower, *why stiled one of the first English poets*, II. 103,
Graces, *Milton improperly misrepresents their birth*, I. 104.
Grayle, Holy, *a tradition concerning it, borrowed from* Morte Arthur, I. 34.

Grayle, II. 243.
Gride, II. 62.
GUILE, *net of, borrowed from Ariosto,* I. 216.

H.

Hair, long, description of, *copied from Chaucer,* I. 182.
 Yellow, *why Spenser always attributes it to his ladies,* II. 48.
Hall, Marshall of, *his Office,* II. 210.
HALL, Bishop, *account of his satires,* I. 134.
HARDYKNUTE, a Scottish poem, *commended,* I. 156.
 Proved to be modern, 156.
HARDING John, *his character,* II. 104.
HARRINGTON, *his versification censured in the translation of Orlando,* I. 122.
Harrow, I. 171.
HAWES, Stephen, *his character,* II. 105. *His works,* 106.
HECATE, *Spenser misrepresents her mythology,* I. 112.
HENRY viii. *improvement of taste and learning in his age,* II. 106.
Hesdin, Castle of, *its tapestry,* I. 177.
HERNE, Thomas, *specimen of his preface to Robert of Glocester,* II. 102.
Hero, Unity of, *necessary in the heroic poem,* I. 6. *Not preserved in the* FAERIE QUEENE, 6. *His business in the heroic poem,* 7.
Herse, and hersal, II. 162.
Him, for himself, II. 251.
HIPPOLITUS, *his story misrepresented,* II. 209.
History, antient, *often falsified by Spenser, and why,* I. 66.
Histories, *a species of drama,* II. 109.
Historical Regularity, *Spenser varies from it, in the plan of the* FAERIE QUEENE, I. 11.
HOLBEIN, Hans, *prints called the Dance of Death, falsly attributed to him,* II. 116. *His picture, so called, at Basil,* II. 117.

(xii)

Horn, a miraculous one, *copied from Ariosto*, I. 201.
HORROR, *picture of him, copied by Milton from Spenser*, I. 76.
Horses *their names in romance*, I. 214.
HUGHES, the editor of Spenser, *censured, for commending the first book of the* FAERIE QUEENE, *as a regular contrivance*, I. 8. *For reducing the text of Spenser to modern orthography*, 121. *A reading of him rejected*, II. 78.
HUON, Sir, *a romance so called*, II. 138.
HURD, Mr. *his sentiments on poetical imitation adopted and commended*, II. 36.
HYLAS, *a new solution concerning his fable*, I. 93.

I.

JAMES I. *Allegory began to decline in his age*, II. 109. *His pedantry vindicated*, 110. *His military genius illustrated*, 162.
Jane, I. 179.
JEALOUSY, Ariosto's, *for what reason so represented*, I. 222.
Jew, character of a cruel and covetous one, *represented on the stage with applause, before Shakespeare's Shylock*, I. 132.
Imitations, *hard to be ascertained*, I. 36. *Spenser's of himself*, 37.
Inconsistency, instances of, *in Spenser*, II. 17.
Indelicacy, *instances of Spenser's*, I. 69.
Inaccuracies, *Spenser guilty of many, and why*, II. 2.
Inn, II. 65.
INO, *Spenser's confused account of her story*, I. 101.
Introduction, form of, *copied from Chaucer*, I. 174. Specimen *of, in old poems*, 181.
Invent, II. 238.
JONSON, Ben, *his opinion of* censured, I. 133. *His sentiments*

(xiii)

Italian language, *deals largely in similar cadences*, I. 113. *Much affected in Q. Elizabeth's time*, 127.
Italian books, *many translated into English in Q. Elizabeth's time*, I. 128. Poets, *censured*, I. 2. *Vindicated*, II.
JUVENAL, *copied by Spenser*, II. 258.

K.

Kenelworth, Castle of, *its round table*, I. 28.
Kings and Kesars, II. 212.

L.

L. D. I. 195.
LADY OF THE LAKE, *the fiction of her, whence borrowed by Spenser*, I. 28. *Introduced to make part of Queen Elizabeth's entertainment at Kenelworth*, 29. *Alluded to by B. Jonson*, 31.
Lair, II. 182.
LANE, John, *account of him*, I. 155.
LONGLANDE, *author of Pierce Plowman's Visions*, II. 213.
Lubber-fiend, I. 120.
LUCRETIUS, *where exceeded by Spenser*, II. 204.
LYDGATE, *character of*. II. 103.

M.

Make and Marr, II. 80.
MALBECCO, *his escape, copied from Ariosto*, I. 209.
MAHOUND, *a character on our stage*, II. 227.
MALEGER, *his death, copied from Ariosto*, I. 206.
Many, I. 195.
MAROT, Clement, *imitated by Spenser*, I. 219.
MARSTON, John, *his satires commended*, I. 59. *Inferior to Hall's*, 59. *Specimen of them*, 59.
Marte, I. 162.
MATERASTA, *name of her castle, drawn from Morte Arthur*, I. 40.

VOL. I. * c

(xiv)

MASQUES, Milton indebted to one for a thought, II. 92. Spenser's imitation of them, 93. Specimen of their machinery, II. 94.

Meseemeth, II. 10.

Merchant of Venice, drawn from an old ballad, I. 128.

MERLIN, story concerning him, borrowed by Spenser from Morte Arthur, a romance, I. 33. His interview with Britomart copied from Ariosto, 208.

MILTON, explained, corrected, illustrated, I. 36, 37, 75, 76, 77, 78, 104, 109, 120, 121, 153, 187, 188. II. 12, 22, 51, 59, 63, 72, 86, 112, 115, 122, 126, 135, 141, 147, 148, 150, 160, 163, 164, 174, 177, 178, 181, 183, 201, 206, 207, 228, 230, 237, 241, 242, 249, 253, 254, 255, 256, 257, 260.

Mirror, Britomart's, borrowed from Chaucer, I. 148. Mirror of Magistrates, criticism upon, and account of, II. 108.

Mis, II. 60.

Misrule, lord of, account of, II. 211.

Monasteries, dissolution of, bad effects of, II. 247.

MONTESQUIEU, his character of the English poets, I. 15.

Morte Arthur, an old romance, printed by Caxton, imitated by Spenser, I. 19. A fashionable book in Queen Elizabeth's time, 27. Alluded to by Ben Jonson, 35. And by Camden, 35.

Moralize, II. 114.

MORE, Sir Thomas, a pageant composed by him, II. 47.

Most and least, I. 191.

More and lesse, I. 191.

Much and lite, I. 191.

MURTHER, Milton's description of him, equalled by Fletcher, I. 77.

MUSÆUS, copied by Spenser, II. 200.

Mythology, antient, falsified by Spenser, and why, I. 66.

N.

NATALIS COMES, *Spenser copies the Deities present at the marriage of Thames and Medway, from him,* I. 103.
NATURE, *description of her, copied from Chaucer,* I. 160.
Negatives, two for an affirmative, *used by Chaucer, after the Saxon practice,* I. 195.
NEREUS, *represented according to Mythology, by Spenser,* I. 103.
NIGHT, *justly represented by Spenser,* I. 73. *Milton supposed to have taken a hint from Spenser's representation of her,* 75.
Nobility, ancient, *their magnificence,* II. 211. *How diminished,* 211.
NOVEMBER, &c. *copied from Chaucer,* I. 161.

O.

OBERON, King Henry viii. I. 57.
OLD AGE, *figures of,* II. 180.
OLLYPHANT, a name, *borrowed from Chaucer,* I. 179.
OPHION, *said to be of the serpent race, by Apollonius, as well as by Milton,* I. 105.
Ordeal, a word, *applied from Chaucer,* I. 191.
ORLANDO FURIOSO, *its plan more irregular than that of the* FAERIE QUEENE, I. 12. *Hint of its hero's madness, drawn from* Morte Arthur, *a Romance,* I. 40.
ORPHEUS, *author of the Argonautics, falsely so called,* I. 100.
ORPHEUS, *his song in Onomacritus and Apollonius, alluded to by Milton,* I. 109. *His song in Apollonius, often alluded to by Spenser,* 105.
Orthography, *often violated by Spenser, and other ancient poets, for the rhyme-sake,* I. 119.
ORTHRUS, I. 102.

(xvi)

P.

Pageants, antient, *influenced the genius of Spenser,* II. 89. *Ridiculed by Cervantes,* 89. *Poetically constructed,* 90.
Pastorals, *fashionable in Spenser's age, and why,* I. 218.
PASTORELL, *her distress, copied from Ariosto,* I. 217.
Peers, Charlemagne's twelve, *account of them,* I. 185. *Alluded to by Milton,* 187.
PLAN, *of the* FAERIE QUEENE, *what,* I. 4. *Its faults,* 5.
PLATO, *copied by Spenser,* I. 88.
POPE, *imitates Jonson,* II. 12. *His false satire in ridiculing Caxton,* 265. *His translation of Homer injurious to true taste,* I. 198.
Powder, II. 158. *In what sense applied by Milton,* 160.
PIERS PLOWMAN's *Crede, account of,* II. 217.
Poets, old english, *how to be criticised,* II. 264.
Poetry, *use and nature of it in the early ages,* I. 106.
Port, II. 242.
Prest, II. 66.
Prick, *to,* I. 194.
PROSERPINE, *her garden, Spenser falsifies mythology concerning it,* I. 80.
Pretended, II. 258.
Proverbs, *copied from Chaucer,* I. 171.
PRYNNE, *specimen of his Histriomastix,* II. 235.
Puritans, *censured by Spenser,* II. 234. *Enemies to literature,* 236.
Purple Island, *of Fletcher, account of,* II. 111.
Pyned, I. 173.

Q.

Queint, II. 256.
Quest, II. 166.
Questyn beast, *mentioned in* Morte Arthur, *a Romance, the origin of Spenser's blatant beast,* I. 22.

R.

RADEGONDE, and her city, *copied from Ariosto,* I. 224.
REAL manners, *copied by Spenser,* II. 88.
Rebellion, grand, *its consequences,* II. 236.
Recreant, II. 147.
Revelations, book of, *Spenser copied from it,* II. 98.
Rhyme, *the advantages found by Spenser in the frequent repetition of it,* I. 117. *He seldom makes the same word rhyme to itself,* I. 122.
Romances, *the* FAERIE QUEENE, *formed upon them,* I. 17. *Fashionable in Queen Elizabeth's age,* I. 18. II. 88. *Caxton's recommendation of them,* I. 42. *Much studied and admired by Milton,* I. 188. II. 33. *Peculiar species of, principally copied by Spenser,* 84. *New hypothesis, concerning the origin of their fictions,* I. 64. 204.
Romans, french, II. 41.
ROMEO and JULIET, *much esteemed when first acted,* I. 69.
ROWLAND, W. *his satires,* I. 60.
Rustic, II. 61.

S.

Sad, II. 116.
Sails, for wings, II. 206.
SANDRART, *mistaken concerning Hans Holbein,* II. 119.
SANGREAL, I. 34, 45. *Manuscript histories of,* II. 243.
SCALIGER, *censured for preferring the song of Orpheus in Apollonius to that in Val. Flaccus,* I. 106. *Prefers a comparison in Apollonius to one in Val. Flaccus,* 95. *Specimen of his criticism on Homer,* 95. *Ignorant of the nature of antient Poetry,* 96.
SCUDAMORE, *whence derived,* II. 190.
Sed, for *said,* I. 120.
Sent II. 72.
Seven Champions of Christendom, Romance of, *imitated by Spenser,* I. 18. 51. II. 123. 128. 129. 137. 167. 174. 178.

𝔖𝔥𝔢𝔭𝔥𝔢𝔯𝔡'𝔰 𝔎𝔞𝔩𝔢𝔫𝔡𝔞𝔯, *title of a book printed by Wynkin a Worde,* I. 125. *Thence adopted by Spenser,* 125.

SHAKESPEARE, *explained and illustrated,* I. 41. 53. 60. 124. 128. 133. 168. 171. 193. II. 39. 41. 87. 109. 145. 158. 183. 229.

𝔖𝔥𝔢𝔢𝔫𝔢, *made a substantive by Milton,* II. 182.

Shew, dumb, in Tragedy, *Spenser alludes to it,* II. 93. *Account of it,* 93.

Shield, a miraculous one, *copied from Ariosto,* I. 200.

𝔖𝔥𝔦𝔫𝔢, II. 181.

Ship of fools, a Poem, II. 106.

Squier's Tale, *Spenser's use of it,* I. 151. *Not unfinished,* 151. *Milton's allusion to it explained,* 153. *A complete copy of it probably seen by Lydgate,* 154. *Completed by John Lane,* 155.

Squire, of Dames, Tale of, *copied from Ariosto,* I. 205. Of lo degree, *title of an old Romance,* II. 183.

SILIUS ITALICUS, *copies from Onomacritus,* I. 109.

SKELTON, *his character,* II. 107. *Explained,* 243.

SKINNER, *his censure of Chaucer's language,* I. 131.

𝔖𝔨𝔯𝔢𝔢𝔫, II. 209.

Sonnets, *two of Spenser's newly discovered,* II. 245.

𝔖𝔬𝔯𝔱, I. 69.

Spear, a miraculous one, *copied from Ariosto,* I. 206.

SPENSER, *anecdote relating to his death,* II. 251.

SPEGHT, *editor of Chaucer, vindicated,* I. 195.

𝔖𝔭𝔢𝔱𝔱, II. 147.

Stanza, Spenser's, *why chosen by him,* I. 113. *Disagreeable to the nature of the English tongue,* 113. *Productive of many absurdities,* 114. *And of some advantages,* 115.

𝔖𝔱𝔦𝔢, I. 64.

STREMONA, *a name of a place no where found,* I. 72.

𝔖𝔲𝔤𝔯𝔢𝔡, II. 145.

Surprise, a fine one, *copied from Chaucer,* I. 144.

(xix)

Swords, named, I. 115.
SYLVANUS, *misrepresented*, I. 72.

T.

TALUS, drawn from Talus, or Talos, *an antient guardian of Crete*, I. 97.
Tales, romantic and humourous, *what formerly fashionable*, II. 39.
TANAQUIL, Queen Elizabeth, I. 58.
TANTALUS, *Spenser misrepresents his Mythology*, I. 80.
TASSO, *his prejudices in favour of romance*, I. 3. *Why Spenser chose rather to imitate Ariosto than him*, 4. *Spenser copies a comparison from him*, I. 91.
Tautology, *instances of it in Spenser*, II. 15.
THEOBALD, *a valuable commentator on Shakespeare*, II. 265.
TILTS and TOURNAMENTS, I. 28. 29. 44. II. 110. *When and where first held in England by royal permission*, I. 28. II. 40. Torneamentum, *different from mensa rotunda*, I. 44.
Time, *sentiments concerning it, copied from Chaucer*, I. 157.
TITYRUS, *Chaucer so called by Milton, from Spenser*, I. 124.
THOPAS, Sir, *a poem of Chaucer, sung to the harp in Q. Elizabeth's age*, I. 53. *Supposed to be burlesque*, 139.
Tobacco, *why praised by Spenser*, II. 165.
Trees, description of, *copied by Spenser from Chaucer*, I. 137. *Chaucer's ridicule of such a description in Statius*, 138. *Spenser has avoided the faults of Statius, and others, in his description*, 138.
TRISSINO, *defended*, I. 2.
TRISTRAM, Sir, *his birth and education, drawn from a Romance called* Morte Arthur, I. 19.
Thebes, siege of, *a favorite story in romance*, I. 175.
TROY, destruction of, *a favorite story in romance*, I. 175. *Caxton's history so called*, I. 224.
TURPIN, *specimen of his history*, I. 215.

(xx)

V.

VALERIUS FLACCUS, *finely describes the distress of Hercules, on losing Hylas*, I. 94.
VENUS, *of both sexes*, I. 96.
Virelayes, *account of*, II. 168.
VIRGIL, *copied by Spenser*, II. 131. 145. 149. *In what excellent*, 202.
Visions of Pierce Plowman, *account of them*, II. 212. *Style of them imitated by Spenser*, I. 125.

U.

UNA, *an Irish name*, II. 124.
Unity, *of action, wanted in the* FAERIE QUEENE, I. 6.
UPTON, Mr. *supposed to have mistaken a passage in Spenser*, I. 101. *In Chaucer*, II. 132.
Ure and enure, II. 241.

W.

WALLER, *imitates Daniel*, II. 107.
Wench, II. 146.
Whole, *necessary to the heroic poem*, I. 8.
Winchester, Marchioness of, *her death celebrated by Milton and Jonson*, II. 12. *Arthur's round table there*, I. 43.
Woman, *praise of, copied from Ariosto*, I. 207.
WOLSEY, Cardinal, *his state*, II. 10.
Wound, *copied from Chaucer*, I. 150.

E R R A T A.

Vol. I. pag. 14. l. 20. read---*but by.* Vol. II. pag. 138. l. 3. for SAXON *Gothic*, read---*Gothic* SAXON.

OBSERVATIONS
ON THE
FAIRY QUEEN
OF
SPENSER.

By THOMAS WARTON, *M. A.*
FELLOW of TRINITY-COLLEGE, and PROFESSOR of POETRY
in the UNIVERSITY of OXFORD.

THE SECOND EDITION,
Corrected and Enlarged.

VOL. I.

GREENWOOD PRESS, PUBLISHERS
NEW YORK

Originally published in 1762 by R. and J. Dodsley

First Greenwood Reprinting, 1968

Library of Congress Catalog Number: 68-31011

Reprinted from a copy in the collections of
the New York Public Library, Astor, Lenox
and Tilden Foundations

PRINTED IN THE UNITED STATES OF AMERICA